THE NEGLECT OF SCIENCE

SCIENCE

Essays Addressed to Laymen

BY

F. E. SIMON, C.B.E., F.R.S.

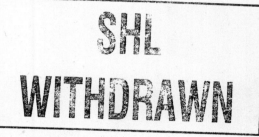

BASIL BLACKWELL
OXFORD
1951

Printed in Great Britain for BASIL BLACKWELL & MOTT, LIMITED
by A. R. MOWBRAY & CO. LIMITED, London and Oxford

FOREWORD

THE world to-day is moulded, in the last resort, by scientific discovery. Research proceeds at an ever-increasing speed; the time needed to translate fundamental discovery into technical achievement is shrinking rapidly; whether we like it or not, science is forcing the pace.

If these developments are not to get out of hand and if we want to make the best use of them, the general public *must* have some understanding of science. At present they certainly have not—politicians perhaps least of all. It is true that very many people learn something about 'gadgets' but we should not mistake the suburbs of science for science itself.

Some people are even proud of their ignorance of science. This may be to some extent a reaction against its misuse, which is now so obvious all over the world; it seems to me, however, that such people take the ostrich as their mascot and are themselves largely responsible for the present unsatisfactory state of affairs. While the world should certainly not be *run* by scientists, we must nevertheless learn how to fit science into our pattern of life. The present world conflict may well be won by those who first succeed in doing this.

Most of the articles in this book have appeared in the *Financial Times* during the last two or three years. They do not attempt to teach science; this would demand more serious work than can be expected of a newspaper reader. They simply try to describe how some of the latest developments affect us in our everyday lives and what is needed if science is to fulfil its promise to help us. They are addressed particularly to readers in this country, for although British science has always held a leading position in the world, science has more often than not been regarded here as a luxury. In the past, when Britain's political predominance gave her easy access to the world's markets, industry could afford to hold these views. Now, however, our industries are having to struggle hard to compete with technologically more advanced countries and they can only succeed if they give up their traditional neglect of science. If this is not done, our standard of living is bound to fall grievously. This theme (though by no means the only one) returns in the articles again and again and has given the title to the book. Another recurring theme, which is, of course, only one aspect of the larger one, is that the economical production and use of power has a very special importance for us.

The articles are printed more or less in the form in which they first appeared in the *Financial Times*. A small number of paragraphs deleted by the Editor— either on account of pressure on his space, or, more rarely, because some of my remarks were thought to be too frivolous—have here been restored. Some of the titles have been changed, editorial sub-titles have been left out, and in a few cases, where the articles had been written rather hurriedly, stylistic alterations have been made. I have not attempted to re-edit the articles; the fact that as now collected they contain a certain amount of repetition is, I think, outweighed by their greater individual coherence and 'bite' in their present form. My sincere thanks are due to Dr. G. O. Jones, a former collaborator of mine and now Reader in Experimental Physics in the University of London, who gave me much assistance in the preparation of the articles, and who also undertook the difficult task of polishing up my English without altering the sense and general style.

I have had encouragement and support from many friends and colleagues, especially from Sir Wallace Akers, Sir James Chadwick, Sir John Cockcroft, Sir Charles Darwin, Dr. G. L. Kelley, Mr. J. R. Park, Mr. M. W. Perrin, Dr. J. C. Swallow, and Sir Henry Tizard; above all am I indebted to Lord Cherwell for our frequent discussions, particularly on the subject of technological education. Needless to say, however, I alone take responsibility for the views expressed.

Finally, I wish to thank the Directors and the Editor of the *Financial Times* for giving me a free hand and for allowing me to publish these articles in book form. I should like to mention particularly the late Mr. Hargreaves Parkinson, who was Editor when I began contributing to the *Financial Times*, and who first suggested that the articles should be brought together in a book.

F. E. SIMON

CLARENDON LABORATORY
OXFORD
May, 1951

CONTENTS

THE NEGLECT OF SCIENCE

THE NEGLECT OF SCIENCE[1]

IT is now a commonplace to say that the science of to-day is the technology of to-morrow. This would not always have been true. In the past science usually followed technical developments, being encouraged to do so by the needs of technology. These were the times when British industry was the best in the world.

Nowadays, however, the progress of technology depends almost entirely on scientific developments. We need mention only a few examples. There would have been no atomic energy if there had not already existed a solid foundation of knowledge in pure physics. To a slightly lesser degree this is true also in electrical engineering.

As a result of our growing fundamental knowledge of the structure of matter the chemical industry has now reached the stage where substances can be built to order to satisfy special requirements. Metallurgy has reached a similar stage, and the pharmaceutical industry depends entirely upon a thorough understanding of chemistry and physiology. The times of purely empirical development are over, although, of course, there is still room for art as well as science in industrial processes.

It is well known that in the past British science led the world, or was at least in the front line, and this is still the case; one might therefore have expected the

[1] *Financial Times*, June 28, 29, 30, 1948.

same to be true in industrial developments. Unfortunately it is only too obvious that this has not been so for many years. Most of the really important industrial developments of this century, such as, for instance, plastics, the fixation of nitrogen, the hydrogenation of coal, and the cracking of heavy oils, were originated in other countries.

The sorry story of the aniline dyes is only too well known, and more recently the production of penicillin has also been allowed to slip out of our hands. Again, industry has failed to follow the cue given by scientific developments in the optical and photographic fields. The role of this country, which formerly led in the development of prime movers, has been lost, the internal-combustion engines, including the Diesel-engine, and the stationary gas turbine having been pioneered in other countries. These examples could be multiplied only too easily.

What are the reasons for this state of affairs? Let us see which countries have overtaken us. Most obviously, of course, America and pre-war Germany, but even Switzerland and Holland have beaten us in limited fields. Can it be that these countries produce better engineers than we do? This would be a severe reproach to the technical education of a country of born engineers!

Could it be that the scientists in these countries are more interested in practical problems than British scientists? This can certainly not be the reason; if proof were needed, we have only to look at the striking scientific developments during the war. When the urgent need appeared, scientists applied themselves with outstanding vigour and success to practical problems of all kinds, and many examples of this are still fresh in our minds. We need only mention a few of these, such as Radar, the part played by British scientists in the development of the atomic bomb, gas turbines for aircraft and jet propulsion, and perhaps the most striking example, 'operational research.'

No! The trouble was that there appeared to be no urgent need for new developments, or at least industry believed that there was no such need. British industry had no difficulty in finding markets because of the political strength of this country. The spirit of enterprise vanished and reappeared in other countries like Germany, America, and Switzerland, who had to conquer their markets.

Thus, accelerated by a tendency to cartellization, we slid slowly but surely into our present state, which can only be described as one of technological backwardness. Of course, there are honourable exceptions; some industries—for instance, the aircraft industry and parts of the chemical industry—have kept the pioneering spirit alive, but this does not alter the general picture.

Designs have become old-fashioned, and equipment has been allowed to become obsolete. It is true that British products have always shown exceptionally good workmanship, but mass-production methods have now also achieved a very high standard.

British industrial firms have in the last fifty years largely changed into financial undertakings, being run by financiers and accountants. These are, of course, an essential part of the machine, but they should not exclude technical and scientific experts from positions of authority. The technical expert or scientist is too often called in only to give an answer to a specific technical question, without having any say in important decisions. 'On tap, but not on top.' (Incidentally, this attitude towards scientists has pervaded British life in other fields also; the Civil Service still suffers from it, much to its detriment.)

The situation was quite different in the young and developing industries abroad, where scientists and technicians were strongly represented on the Boards— perhaps not always quite as strongly as in the famous German chemical trust I.G.; this body was largely built up and run by scientists—and did quite well out of it!

After two world wars conditions are quite changed. This country has lost its political domination, and the situation is aggravated by the loss of foreign investments. We now have to compete seriously with people who have been accustomed to free competition, and who have built up their industries accordingly.

If we want to survive and to pay our way without outside help, we shall have to export industrial products which can compete on the markets of the world, even when the present sellers' market is over. Our position now is similar in many ways to that of Switzerland, which has few raw materials, cannot produce sufficient food, and never had political influence on the market. Like Switzerland we have to manufacture high quality products of advanced design at competitive prices, but, of course, on a much larger scale.

The facts outlined above, though somewhat over-simplified, seem to be indisputable. But there have been many other results of our past comparative freedom from competition, such as the persistence of antiquated production methods. Again, the poor salesmanship shown by British firms abroad has become quite notorious. These topics are outside the scope of these articles, and we shall limit ourselves to a discussion of the role which should be played by science in Britain's industrial recovery.

THE INDUSTRIAL RESEARCH LABORATORY

There are various ways in which science can be brought to influence industrial development; for instance, by direct contact between private firms and university scientists, by the work in Government departments, or by the research associations of industrial groups. By far the most important part must, however, under the existing system of private enterprise, be played by the research laboratories of the individual firms.

While, of course, there were some firms which made full use of research laboratories, in most cases these played only a very minor role. Research facilities were generally quite insufficient; quite frequently the laboratory was only a test laboratory, given the more impressive name of a research laboratory, and sometimes even large and important firms confessed quite unashamedly to possessing no laboratories—they relied on buying patents abroad, thinking that they could economize in this way!

What should be the functions of an industrial research laboratory? First let us be clear that such a laboratory should not be merely an ordinary test laboratory, which, of course, every firm needs for checking the quality of its materials and products. Neither should it be concerned mainly with fundamental research; this can be left to the universities which are better equipped for it.

It is true that a certain amount of real fundamental research is also useful to a firm because it means that there will always be people available who are in touch with the latest developments in science. However, this can in general be expected only in the case of the largest firms.

The main business of the industrial research laboratory must be to produce and develop ideas which can be of practical value to the firm. These ideas may be concerned with the immediate improvement of existing processes and products, with more fundamental changes in the processes, with finding new uses for existing products, or with developing completely new products and new ideas.

Obviously some of these objectives are of a long-term character and it is one of the main jobs of the research director to keep a proper balance. Apart from the conception of new ideas and their first trials, work is generally seen through in the research laboratory to what is often called the 'semi-technical' stage, where the new process is carried out on a somewhat larger scale to give first ideas about the technical or economic practicability of the process.

Naturally during the research and the semi-technical period many different trails are followed; some of these are bound to lead to disappointments and new ideas often have to be abandoned altogether. When, however, an idea leaves the research laboratory, it should be in such a state that it can more or less be taken over by the departments responsible for the pilot plant and later stages. The research laboratory can thus be regarded as providing the spearhead of every new development.

It is clear from what has been said that an industrial research laboratory must not be regarded as an isolated unit, but must form an organic part of the whole organization. Exchange of information with other departments, such as the production, sales, and accounts departments, is essential and should be supplemented by frequent exchanges of personnel. It goes without saying that the research department must be completely informed of the general policy of the firm.

Nothing can be more demoralizing to a department—and this not infrequently happens—than to have developed a new process up to the pilot plant stage and then to hear that it does not fit the company's policy, or cannot be carried through for some other reason. The only certain way to avoid this danger is to make sure that a scientist or engineer-scientist is a member of the Board; this will usually be the Director of Research, who can then not only represent the point of view of the laboratory but also get all the information needed to allow him to direct his department properly.

There is another point of importance. One wants those scientists who are not occupied with routine work to have ideas, and these cannot be produced to order. A scientist must sometimes be able to sit back for a few weeks, perhaps without obvious signs of activity, to do some thinking. 'Clocking in and out' does not create the right atmosphere; many firms try to apply their ordinary rules of discipline to the research laboratory, and this is a mistake. These matters have been discussed in some detail to make it clear that it is not enough simply to put a few scientists on the pay-roll and then to wait for the 'goose that lays the golden eggs' to produce results—preferably within a year or two.

Fortunately in the last few years before the war there were moves in the right direction. The development of the plastic 'polythene' was a very good example of the imaginative application of research in industry. Recently, as a result of the lessons learnt during the war, there has been a further change in industry's attitude towards research, particularly now it has been realized that most of the really new developments during the war came from universities and not from industrial firms.

More technical men have been appointed to Boards, and some firms, at least, have started to build up new research departments. The Federation of British Industries is well aware of the urgent need for research and has formed a very active committee which has already done most useful work.

Very much, however, remains to be done, particularly in the older industries. How much we lag behind can be seen from the figures of expenditure on research and on the early stages of development. It is not easy to find a proper yard-stick against which to measure effort spent on research, nor is it easy even to define how much is spent on it in any particular case as there is often no sharp line between the testing laboratory and the research laboratory proper, nor between the early and later stages of development.

It would seem to be a pretty fair estimate if we say that firms in the front line of technical advance in the countries already mentioned generally spend about 3 to 5 per cent of their turnover on research. Only a very few firms in this country spend as much as this. On the average about a half to a third as much is spent here compared with countries with a progressive industry. Such a figure must not, of course, be taken too strictly. In some fields firms will spend more, and there are other cases where less research may be needed. As a rough and ready rule, however, one can say that an investor should not risk his money without careful examination in a firm which spends much less than this amount, particularly if at the same time the firm has no scientific or technical expert on its Board.

Let us consider what would happen if all our backward firms recognized the need for research laboratories. Would they be able to put them into operation quickly? It has already been emphasized that a research laboratory must be an organic part of the whole organization and it therefore cannot really grow up in a few years' time, even in the right atmosphere.

The greatest difficulty, however, is the shortage of the right kind of people. Of course, Britain has potentially available all the people who would be needed, being probably better provided than any other country in this respect. During the long period of neglect of industrial research, however, a number of things have happened which cannot now be easily repaired.

First, as a result of the dearth of responsible and highly paid positions in industry a large number of people with an interest in applied science have left the country. It was a shock to many who worked in America during the war to see how many first-class British applied scientists had crossed the Atlantic between the wars and were now in high industrial positions in America; these people should now have been among our research directors or in other important positions, and are badly missed.

Secondly, this lack of demand for trained scientists and engineers has not only led to their flowing-off into other channels, but has also had a profound influence on our higher educational institutions. It is true that education should anticipate new developments and not lag behind, but that does not in fact seem to happen anywhere in the world; it would in any case be asking a lot of our educational institutions to foresee when industry would be likely to change its outlook and to prepare a new generation for positions which at the time did not exist. It is no wonder, therefore, that the right type and number of educational institutions simply do not exist to serve our present needs.

If we now discuss the educational question we must widen our field and consider not only people suitable for research laboratories, but the whole field of scientific education. This includes the question of training scientists for positions in universities and research laboratories, the teachers of science for schools and technical institutes, the applied scientists who mainly find their place in industry, and finally the engineers proper who of course again are mainly employed in industry, generally on purely practical jobs.

There is not much to say about the universities, at least about those departments which are concerned with pure science. It is true that they have lacked support from industry, which has played a great part in America in building up university research laboratories. This lack of interest has also led to the neglect of some subjects, such as, for instance, inorganic chemistry. It is also true that the total number of scientists produced by the universities is insufficient to supply the demands. On the whole, however, one can say that the kind of education offered by the universities is satisfactory.

The real shortcomings are in the field of technical education. Let us first have a look at technical education in countries which have had progressive industries. We will find that most of their engineers or applied scientists have been educated at colleges of technology, first introduced in Germany as 'Technische Hochschulen' about a hundred years ago. These are institutions of university standing which, in courses lasting four or five years, give their students really thorough education in the fundamental sciences and at the same time in some particular specialized field of engineering.

Theory and experiment are generally properly balanced and these institutes are very well supplied with laboratories in which practical experience can be gained. In addition to this, however, up to about 20 per cent of the student's time is devoted to training in other subjects which are of essential importance to the practical man, such as, for instance, economics, labour relations, psychology, and so on.

Perhaps the most famous of these institutes in Europe is the Institute of Technology at Zürich, which, apart from nearly 100 full professors, employs about the same number of associate and assistant professors and 150 assistants for an undergraduate body of roughly 2,000; that is, one highly-trained teacher for every six undergraduates. Very similar to it is the Institute of Technology at Delft which provides for the needs of Holland.

The Institutes of Technology in America are justly famous; for instance, the Massachusetts, California, and Carnegie Institutes of Technology, to name only a few. In addition, most of the really large universities in the U.S.A. have departments of technology which are themselves so big that they lead a more or less independent life and are about equivalent to the Institutes of Technology already mentioned. Curiously enough, the main difference seems to be that the Institutes of

B

Technology actually put more emphasis on the fundamental sciences and their graduates are for that reason sometimes preferred by industry.

All these institutions carry out extensive research in the field of engineering and also in pure science. Naturally this purely scientific work is somewhat differently oriented from that carried out in university departments, where the emphasis is directed towards that which at any particular time appears to give the highest promise of increasing fundamental knowledge. Thus, at present most university physics laboratories all over the world are engaged in work on nuclear physics. That this should be so is in itself quite right, but the consequences are that big stretches in other fields of greater immediate practical importance are denuded. The research departments of the Institutes of Technology concentrate their interest more on these latter fields, fulfilling in this respect a very important task.

Thus, in the industrially advanced countries we find Institutes of Technology able to keep up with the needs of industry, giving first-class training in the scientific fundamentals, and branching out into many important fields of applied science. Now what is the position here? In this country we have no Institutes of Technology; perhaps the nearest approach we have is the Imperial College in London.

The technical education of engineers and applied scientists of university level is mainly left to the rather small engineering departments attached to the universities. Nearly all these departments are much too small to offer the variety of educational facilities, particularly the use of laboratories, open to the more fortunate students in the other countries. Again, the length of the training course is generally only three years. Of course, in some of these university technical departments extremely good work is done—how could it be otherwise?—but as a whole the technical education provided is definitely inferior to that offered abroad.

Considering our relative populations as compared with Switzerland, we may say that this country ought to possess ten 'Zürich' institutes. It is quite obvious not only that this quantity of teaching capacity does not exist here, but also that there is not a single institution in this country approaching in quality the Zürich Institute.

The remainder of our engineers receive their education at technical colleges, often by preparing themselves in evening classes for external degrees. There are about 200 of these colleges of varying quality, none of them up to university standard, most of them very much below. While these may be suitable for the education of technicians—though even in this respect they generally do not compare too favourably with their opposite numbers abroad—they are wholly unsuitable for educating engineers of the type with which we are concerned here. Hardly any of these colleges carry out any research worth the name and this alone is enough to show that they cannot have people on their teaching staffs really able to supply proper training in their subjects.

The fact that we have good engineers in this country says much for the native skill of the British. It must be said that this is largely in spite of, rather than because of, our educational institutions, which are hardly in a position to produce the type and certainly not the numbers of applied scientists we need for the invigoration of our industry. (The Barlow Report has estimated that the numbers should be doubled.)

The training given in fundamentals is poor. In the past some fields have been badly neglected—production engineering is a very important case. There is a most serious shortage in the field of chemical engineering, which threatens to strangle some of our essential industrial developments. This has a particularly unfortunate effect at the pilot plant stage of chemical developments, a stage in which the Americans have become such masters—as we saw, for instance, in the remarkably fast development of the atomic bomb and in their large-scale manufacture of penicillin.

The picture which we have drawn here is a sombre one. There is certainly no easy way out of the position we find ourselves landed in and one sometimes wonders how we can deal with it at all. The technical superiority of America in particular and the rate of expansion there is frightening; while we are still so short of engineer-scientists here, they speak of rapidly multiplying their present high numbers; they have a large number of engineering schools in existence able to turn out people of types which are obviously essential and which hardly exist in this country.

The Russians, it is true, are still far behind but with the enormous effort now being pumped into expanding their scientific and educational institutions, and with their innate ability, which should not be underrated, they are bound to make rapid progress.

The great asset this country has is the excellence of the human material and its specific ability in the fields of science and engineering—supported by the native team-spirit. With the proper outlook in education and in industry a really supreme effort could redress the adverse balance. But the job will be a most difficult one and cannot be tackled by patchwork or half-hearted methods.

What ought to be done? Obviously we have only discussed a small—though important—part of the whole picture and there are other essential factors, such as the need for a renewed pioneering, or 'buc-caneering' spirit in selling British products. We must not underestimate the hampering effects of restrictions, which sometimes have a serious effect in crippling real enterprise, or of the failure to make full use of machines by running shifts. Also, the whole problem has ob-viously to be considered in the light of the present economic crisis, in which the immediate need for increasing exports competes with capital expenditure.

The obvious immediate step is to make sure that we have proper representation of engineer-scientists on the Boards of companies. They will be able to do a lot in giving science a proper position in industry, but they will find themselves seriously hampered in the job of building up research departments by the lack of suitable people to man them; and there will still be a shortage of high-class engineers for other departments. What can be done about this? Obviously our educa-tional facilities must be enormously expanded and improved in these fields.

This will not apply so much to universities, which are already good, though a certain expansion will be necessary, and should not be too difficult. The real trouble is in technical education, which really does not give a proper chance to the younger generation, and which has to be rebuilt, root and branch.

It would be foolish to suggest that the present institutions should be scrapped. It would be no good, however, simply expanding the present university engineering departments; for one thing, to bring them up to the required level would make them so big that they would throw the whole university out of balance.

What we need are full-blown institutions like Zürich or the Massachusetts Institute of Technology of full university status and demanding high standards, and we should at least build two such Institutes of Technology at once. If we cannot at present get the necessary teachers for some subjects such as chemical engineering, production engineering, or metallurgy, these will have to be imported from abroad. To try to 'save' by limiting ourselves to patching over too obvious short-comings—and unfortunately there seem to be signs that this is being started—would be fatal.[1]

No number of committee reports will help unless the general public is aroused to a realization of the seriousness of the situation. This matter is of vital importance to the whole of the British people and it is up to them to see that something is done about it.

[1] These remarks have been amply justified by more recent develop-ments, especially by the publication of a very unfortunate report drawn up by a committee of the Ministry of Education. This even prompted a paper as mild mannered as *Nature* to advise the minister to 'leave a singularly inept report severely alone.'

FUNDAMENTAL RESEARCH [1]

MANY different activities go under the name 'research.' The writer recently visited a firm where he found that 'our research department' consisted of a young, and admittedly beautiful, lady and her equipment of only a few books of the *Boy's Book of Inventions* type. This is no doubt an extreme case, but there are still not very many companies where research is really taken seriously. While one of the first aims of every firm should be to see that research has its proper place within the organization, we nevertheless have to realize that this is not the whole story.

The real progress of science depends very largely on a relatively small number of people who pursue pure fundamental research, as distinct from the more applied research which directly concerns industry. These pure scientists pursue their investigations because they are curious, without any thought of the possible practical applications of their work.

The fruits of their research increase our knowledge of nature and in time often find applications of great practical importance. Faraday's investigations, for instance, laid the foundations of our present electrical industry. The work of Maxwell and Hertz led to the development of radio, which has completely altered techniques of news-transmission and propaganda, with all their important implications in everyday life and politics.

Thus industry is bound to be interested in the general state of fundamental research. It will be useful

[1] *Financial Times*, May 9, 10, 1949.

to discuss one particular case, that of the release of nuclear energy, in some more detail as this will help us to see what we should and should not do if we want science to advance.

About fifty years ago it was discovered that a photographic plate was darkened when placed near a piece of pitchblende. A very short time before this, X-rays had been discovered, and the new phenomenon was thus taken more seriously than it might have been earlier. In time, the substance responsible for the darkening effect was tracked down, and finally, after much laborious work, isolated in small amounts. More people now became interested; the radiations emitted from this substance, radium, were investigated and their natures discovered.

Independent investigations into the discharges of electricity in gases had led to the identification of several of the particles which build up atoms, particularly the 'electron.' Also, other investigations in an apparently quite unrelated field, the study of heat radiation, had led to the development of a new theory—the 'Quantum Theory'—which explained many properties of the atom which could not be explained by the earlier 'classical' mechanics.

From all these separate sources it became possible to form a picture of the structure of the atom. The atom was now recognized as consisting of a heavy nucleus responsible for the radio-active phenomena, and a 'cloud' of light electrons responsible for most ordinary physical and chemical phenomena. In the following years the nucleus itself was shown to be made up of still smaller particles, the so-called 'protons' and 'neutrons.'

Now another very abstract theory—the 'Theory of Relativity'—entered the picture. This had again arisen out of completely unconnected experiments, into whether absolute motion of the earth could be detected. This theory eventually led to the discovery of a relationship between mass and energy and it was then possible to predict from the masses of certain atoms that rearrangements within their nuclei might lead to the discharge of large amounts of energy.

This network of experiment and theory was made up of the work of hosts of scientists in many countries, none of whom had any thought of possible practical applications. Among them, to mention a few names only, were Becquerel, the Curies, Planck, J. J. Thomson, Rutherford, Moseley, Roentgen, Laue, the Braggs, Michelson, Einstein, Bohr, Chadwick, Joliot, Fermi, Hahn.

We know that the latest step has been the practical release of nuclear energy, still so fresh in our minds. Let us consider the most important consequences of this last development. It has increased our knowledge of the structure of matter, and of the structure of the universe; it led directly to the atomic bomb, and may some day give us a supply of power. It has already led to important new advances in medicine, in the treatment and diagnosis of cancer, for instance, and will fertilize wide fields in the biological and physicochemical sciences by providing powerful new experimental tools, the 'radio-active tracer elements.'

By no stretch of imagination could anyone have predicted the practical consequences of the experiments which started the whole development. Would any Government intending to develop a super-weapon have supported the first experiments on radio-activity fifty years ago—or the relativity theory? Or could any amount of money which a philanthropist might

have put at the disposal of cancer research have
resulted in the discovery of radio-activity?

This does not mean, of course, that money should
not be set aside, say, for the fight against cancer, or that
one should not spend money on the development of
new power sources. Any number of practical problems
still remain in these fields, and most scientists will be
busy with such problems or with the corresponding
practical problems of industrial research. But one
should not expect that any final solution for the treatment or prevention of cancer, say, will necessarily, or
even probably, come from money ear-marked for this
purpose.

Thus we see that fundamental research cannot be
planned. What we can do, however, is to see that
conditions are created under which some scientists
can do fundamental research without too much dis-
turbance. If this is not done, and the vital fountain
is allowed to dry up, it will have, in the long run, most
serious consequences for the country concerned. Since
people and Governments are very often interested only
in the fairly near future, the question of giving adequate
support to fundamental research has hardly ever received the attention it deserves and the general public
in particular knows little about what should be done.

Let us consider what practical steps are possible to
foster fundamental research. Should we build new
laboratories in which scientists could lead sheltered
lives and devote themselves to pure research? This
would mean taking them away from the universities,
where most scientists now work, dividing their time
between teaching and research.

Now although the setting up of a few pure research
laboratories would perhaps be desirable there are

many reasons why one should leave things, broadly speaking, as they are now. The most important reason is that advanced instruction in fields in which the frontiers of science are moving rapidly can only be given by a man who is himself active in research. (We see the results of failure to link teaching and research in the present unsatisfactory position of our technical colleges.) Conversely, the preparation of advanced lectures, and the necessity which it entails of surveying all the literature of his subject, often clarifies a research worker's ideas and gives him new ones.

Again, only an active teacher can pick out from among his pupils those who should be encouraged to do research after taking their degrees, and who eventually might be able to direct research themselves. This question of picking the right people is most important, and in itself a sufficient reason for keeping teaching and research together. If they are separated, the selection of research students has to be based entirely on the results of examinations, and examinations are at present not designed for this, but for the selection of civil servants and teachers.

There are, of course, dangers in the present arrangement, the most important of which is that many scientists may have to devote too much of their time to teaching, particularly at the present time, when there is a great increase in the number of students taking scientific subjects. Very often younger scientists, in particular, are seriously overworked with teaching and have little time left to sit back and do any thinking. A reasonable division, rarely attained in practice, would be about one-quarter teaching, three-quarters research.

Of course, we have to remove all other unnecessary work. Things have improved very much during and since the war, but a lot still remains to be done. Laboratories need much more help on the administrative side. Senior research workers, at least, have too much administrative work and work on committees. Some of this may be unavoidable, but they certainly should not be forced to do the work of secretaries also. Again, all too often we find high-powered scientists doing work in their laboratories which could be done quite well by skilled laboratory assistants or mechanics —a most uneconomical waste of talent. There is already quite enough unavoidable extra work for most scientists without these additional burdens.

We find scientists also too often hampered by lack of funds for apparatus. During the war, when every reasonable demand for equipment was generally satisfied, it became possible to calculate what the total cost (including all salaries) of a properly run laboratory should be, assuming reasonable equilibrium between senior and junior research people, laboratory assistants, mechanics, and clerical help.

This figure ought to be between about £1,200 and £1,500 a year per research worker, excluding the requirements of exceptional equipment such as, for instance, the cyclotron. Any laboratory which has not this amount of money available is simply not making the best use of those rare birds, the first-class research scientists, and at the present time we just cannot afford this. Incidentally, the corresponding figure for research laboratories in industry is, on the average, about three times as high, mainly because each research man needs more helpers to carry out the greater amount of routine work involved.

The next need is for enough permanent positions for these scientists to give them a reasonable feeling of security, with salaries at least adequate to free them of financial worry. These salaries need not, of course, compete with those paid in industry, and university scientists will gladly put up with smaller financial reward in exchange for their increased freedom to choose, and later to publish, their work. But they should at least be able to make both ends meet. Otherwise they will take on additional work of a routine but lucrative nature. We should take a warning example from France where scientists are so badly underpaid that professors often have to take on two or three jobs—with serious consequences to the state of science in that country. Again, Holland is now losing many of its most brilliant young scientists to the United States for the same reason.

In this country the position is not so serious, but the salaries of professors and younger university scientists are definitely below the danger limit and something rather drastic will soon have to be done if we want to make the best use of our scientists, and if the drain to the United States, which is already noticeable—particularly from the ranks of the younger people—is not to become dangerous.[1]

The Americans now realize fully the importance of fundamental research. Although they lead the world in industrial science, they had no great tradition in fundamental research and reached their position by drawing heavily on European ideas—and European scientists. They are now beginning to move ahead rapidly in fundamental research also, but are still trying to attract more and more European scientists.

[1] Since this was written, university salaries have been increased considerably, but we must watch carefully that with rising prices their real value does not slide right back to their previous unsatisfactory level.

Let us now see roughly how much money we require in order to support fundamental research adequately in this country. It has already been said that the real progress of science depends very largely on a relatively small number of scientists. However, they would be almost helpless without the much larger numbers of younger scientists, mostly research trainees taking advanced degrees, who work under their supervision. Their total number in this country at present run into many thousands.

If we multiply by the figure already given for the approximate cost, per scientist, of financing a laboratory, we see that the total amount of money needed is to be counted in millions of pounds per annum— even without further expansion in numbers. It is clear that the universities cannot hope to provide the necessary money, and we also know that young people training for research cannot look after their own expenses as sometimes used to be possible. Before the war, the position was very unsatisfactory in most countries, including our own. The lessons learnt since have led to considerable improvement although the ideal figures mentioned previously are far from being reached.

Only Governments have such large sums at their disposal and there is always the danger that Governments will try to influence the directions of research. This danger has not been avoided everywhere, but the position in Britain is more or less satisfactory. There are no 'strings' attached to the money distributed by the University Grants Committee and the Department of Scientific and Industrial Research (D.S.I.R.), the two main instruments for distributing money from Government sources to the universities. The University

Grants Committee allocates its funds mainly for the general support of universities (including the arts), while the D.S.I.R. provides help for projects of special promise and also provides training grants for research trainees—the Ph.D. students. Without these grants research would now come to a standstill and one can say that everyone who gives reasonable promise of becoming a good research scientist can obtain a research grant for two or three years.

Not so satisfactory are the prospects for the qualified men with a Ph.D. degree. Most of these will, of course, enter industrial research laboratories or similar institutions, and a smaller number will go to the schools as teachers. While there are certainly plenty of openings as school teachers, the salaries offered are so bad that far too few people are attracted to this profession, which forms a most important part of the whole structure of scientific education.

For the others who feel that they must do pure fundamental research the position is still not really satisfactory. There are not enough university posts available which allow the holder to concentrate on research. There is a great opportunity here for private enterprise. Apart from the general help which can be given, it is more likely to be a healthy state of affairs if all the support for science does not come from one source. Scientists are often queer people, and someone who fails to impress some official or a selection committee may yet turn out later to be a genius. Apart from this, too much emphasis is still sometimes put upon particular fields of research by official bodies—often with the best intentions—with consequent detriment to other branches. A very striking example is the over-emphasis which is everywhere placed on nuclear physics at the present time.

A small number of grants for more senior workers have always been available, such as, for instance, those provided by the Royal Society, or the senior research grants of the D.S.I.R. Fortunately, a number of enlightened industrial firms have recently provided funds for the establishment of research fellowships at the universities, and they have rightly stipulated that the holders of these grants should be allowed, or even encouraged, to do a small amount of teaching.

Now what would be the ideal conditions surrounding such a grant? First, there should always be free choice of subject for research, with no ear-marking for special purposes. We need not fear unduly that the scientist will go completely astray as his own instinct will help him to sense the right direction.

There will, of course, be some guidance given by the head of the department, particularly to the younger members of the laboratory. In this matter the finding of the right compromise is a delicate but most important question. There are two extremes. On the one hand, the German example in which the laboratory exists more or less *ad majoram gloriam* of the professor, and on the other the state of affairs in France—and often in America—where laboratories are split up into too many independent units. The balance is perhaps best struck in this country, where people are individualists, but where, nevertheless, the existence of a team spirit prevents the laboratory from breaking up into too small units. This is probably one of the reasons for the high standard of fundamental research in this country.

Another important requirement in the provision of

grants for research is that there should be a fair amount of flexibility in the salaries offered in order to cater for special cases. Now, while the two requirements already mentioned are generally met in practice, this is not the case with the next: it is not enough to provide a salary for the scientist himself, unless the laboratory which takes him on is enabled to provide him with the apparatus or workshop assistance which he needs. Ideally, for every salary grant, a roughly equivalent additional sum should be allocated to the laboratory which has to provide the facilities for research.

There is another reason why anyone who wishes to support fundamental research would do well to see that there are no 'strings' attached to his gift, and to suppress his natural, and justifiable, inclination to want some return for his money. The less he sees of how his gift is spent the better, although this goes against all normal business practice, and might seem to imply an ungenerous attitude on the part of the universities. The fact is, however, that one of the most stultifying influences upon pure research can be the feeling that *results* are awaited by someone. It is easy enough to get plenty of results—by choosing a suitable problem—but that is not how progress is made in science.

Another field in which much can be done—and in this case with relatively modest sums—is in the facilitation of travel for scientists. Free discussion between workers in the same field is one of the most stimulating influences in scientific research, as we can easily see from the sterilizing effect of isolation on scientists in Nazi Germany and present-day Russia. It is obvious, too, from the list of names already given of scientists whose work led to the recent discoveries in connection

C

with atomic energy, how the progress of science is a truly international affair.

Scientists in this country, at least, have at present far too few opportunities of meeting their colleagues abroad. While this is perhaps not so difficult for well-known senior scientists, the situation is very bad indeed for younger scientists, who actually would benefit most from this stimulation. It is astonishing in these times when everyone speaks of building a unified world, or at least a united Europe, that not more thought is put into this matter. While it ought to be possible for scientists to pay frequent visits to their colleagues in neighbouring countries, it is pathetic to see what obstacles have to be overcome in order to finance even a short visit to, say, Holland or France, or to invite a Dutch or French scientist to lecture in this country. The British Council and the Royal Society try to help, but can do so only on a much too small scale. A few hundred pounds per year at the disposal of each of the larger laboratories, and perhaps another central fund for the benefit of scientists from smaller laboratories, would make an enormous difference to the scientific atmosphere.

Finally, some more general remarks. Some people may ask why, when fundamental research published in one country benefits industrial developments all over the world, it is necessary to have fundamental research in all countries? Why not leave it—especially in times of financial stress—to the richer countries? There are many reasons why this negative attitude would be disastrous for any country which adopted it. Quite apart from the question of providing satisfactory education for the practical or applied scientist, we must remember that the scientific community is a living one, with an equilibrium between different types of people. The same is of course true also for the different types of research. It is impossible to neglect fundamental aspects of research without damaging the whole. We should take a warning example from what we see in some other countries. In France, for instance, a country which possesses some of the most brilliant scientific brains, industrial developments have been seriously affected by the failure to provide reasonable conditions of living and work for scientists.

This sort of negative attitude towards science is perhaps one result of a feeling which is growing among many people, that there should be not more, but less science. Many people even think that a 'moratorium' on science should be pronounced all over the world, to give the world's moral or social education an opportunity to catch up with its technical education. The answer to this is that such an idea would be unrealistic unless there existed some means by which it could be enforced in all countries, and if this existed, the need for the moratorium would more or less have disappeared. A better way of reducing the gulf between the world's social and technical education would be to put more emphasis on the social sciences. It would certainly be quite futile to try to stop the progress of the natural sciences. Scientists undertake their researches because they are eager to 'find out.' Their success can be retarded if they are not able to obtain proper facilities. However, a thirsty man who cannot find pure water will drink from a puddle, and funds will always be forthcoming for military developments; if, therefore, we try to retard the progress of scientific research we would lose its benefits without succeeding in our original intention.

We have to realize, therefore, that fundamental research is one of the most important factors in the well-being of every nation, and one which cannot be neglected with impunity. In our own country the position is not too unsatisfactory, though still far from ideal. However, this matter is particularly important for us, since we must now live on our brains, and not on the remnants of our former political power, if we are to re-establish ourselves in the world. We have the human resources necessary to do this and industry has a vital interest in seeing that these resources are fully used. A number of ways in which it can help have already been indicated. But we must also see that we find all our potential scientists and we may hope that the larger field for selection opened up by the new Education Act will soon give us access to resources so far untapped.

AMERICA REVISITED[1]

THE SOCIAL SCENE

The last ten years have seen the United States rise to be the world's most powerful State, and also, its final turning away from isolationism. Indeed, the future of the world must very largely depend on the citizens of the United States and so it is only to be expected that the visitor, even though primarily concerned with scientific and industrial developments, casts an axious eye on the social scene. For cultural and sociological factors must in the long run play an important part in determining a country's internal stability. Thus, before turning to the main topic of these articles a few remarks may be appropriate on some general impressions gained during a stay of two months this autumn, the writer's first visit to America since 1944.

Superficially, little seems to have changed during the past five years. As always, one is impressed by the great energy with which every form of activity is carried on—and this in spite of a very trying climate. Some aspects of this dynamic attitude to life are, however, not entirely admirable, and although the general standard of living is very high, competition is very keen—even in the universities—and life is as exacting as ever; coronary afflictions of the heart have become the occupational disease of the successful man.

One would hardly have expected any lessening in the general pre-occupation with sporting events (incidentally, it is the fast game which attracts, the

[1] *Financial Times*, January 3, 4, 5, 1950.

gambling element being relatively unimportant). Indeed, during the writer's stay, the deeds of the 'Giants' and the 'Red Sox' dominated the headlines, being ousted only for a short interval by the news of the explosion of the Russian atomic bomb.

However, the most general preoccupation, though perhaps no longer at its war-time high, is still with the more primitive aspects of the female form—and the contraptions designed to keep them under proper control. The art of advertising suffers particularly from this. The favourite method of attracting attention to a particular product, whether washing machine, beer, or patent medicine, is still to adorn the advertisement with a 'blonde,' the more salient features (of the girl) being put in proper relief.

Perhaps more disappointing is the fact that Americans still seem to prefer to get their mental food from 'tabloids' or from magazines of the 'True Romances' or crime-thriller type. Appropriately enough, these are dispensed in drug stores, not in bookshops. One still has to search for a long time to find a bookshop, and an average town of 50–100,000 inhabitants will only possess one. Certainly very large numbers of books are printed, but a recent report on the 'Book Industry' (as it is called) has revealed a very far from pleasant picture. Publishing firms are on the way to becoming factories for the production of 'best-sellers'— frequently produced with the help of ghost writers— and the enormous editions of these books, often distributed by book clubs, undermine the chances of books which do not happen to conform to the current general pattern. This is yet a further step towards the uniformity to which film and radio (and now television) have already made such a great contribution.

What gives the visitor his worst shock, however, are the so-called 'comic strip' sections in the newspapers. To the uninitiated, at least, it seems that these must be intended for people who cannot read sentences containing more than a few words. Their grip on the general public, however, appears to be as strong as ever, and one hears that only one daily newspaper has succeeded in keeping them out of its columns.

That comic-strip addicts should be able to determine the future of the world must certainly appear disquieting. However, first impressions are sometimes deceptive, particularly in times of rapid development. It has often happened that the ideas and tastes of the people have developed more quickly than realized by those whose professional concern it is to judge them. Indeed, one feels after private discussions, not only with highly educated people, but with, say, cab drivers or shop assistants, that at least some Americans are beginning to wonder whether all is well with the American way of life. A few people are even beginning to doubt the old 'Victorian' belief, so simple and convenient, and up to now so universally accepted in America, that progress is inevitable, and that everything would be all right if only everybody would behave as they, the Americans, do.

One problem in particular has shaken the confidence of many people—that of the coloured population. This certainly poses most serious questions for the future, questions which do not seem to have a ready answer. Again, many people have been deeply worried by the reports of the recent proceedings of the Congressional Committee investigating so-called 'un-American activities.' This has brought into relief the dangerous wish of many Americans to establish uniformity by the suppression of unpopular opinions—indeed, although the methods used are different, the ultimate result would be a similar uniformity to that found in the totalitarian States.

Though the number of doubters may not yet be very large, there is one group, and that an important one, which seems to be deeply stirred. These are the scientists. Rightly or wrongly, they feel responsible for the atomic bomb. As one of the leaders of the Atomic Energy Project has expressed it: 'In some sort of crude sense, which no vulgarity, no humour, no over-statement can quite extinguish, the physicists have known sin; and this is a knowledge which they cannot lose.'

Even those who have no scruples about the military use of atomic energy continue to leave the Atomic Energy Project in great numbers because of the close secrecy restrictions imposed on them by the military authorities, and the former chairman of the United States Atomic Energy Commission, David Lilienthal, has stated that this was the reason for his resignation. The scientific spirit cannot long survive in this atmosphere, and although there are some fields in which secrecy is obviously necessary in present circumstances (actually these are mainly the technical rather than the scientific aspects of the subject), secrecy has been very much overdone in America. At the present moment there is a more or less universal rebellion against it, and a recent statement issued by the American Chemical Society is typical: 'If we are to maintain our supremacy over the next few critical years, we must revise our approach—not alone on our attitude toward secrecy, but on other questions of policy. That secrecy means

security is a false notion that may lead us down a path
to possible destruction.'[1]

This is not the only thing worrying the scientists.
They also rightly object to the fact that a very high
proportion of the money spent on research of all kinds
now comes from military sources. While it must be
admitted that this money, particularly that provided
by the Navy, is at present distributed very fairly and
with no strings—or practically no strings—attached,
it is difficult to see why Government funds for science
in general should be distributed by the military, and
the situation is obviously fraught with danger.

As a whole this developing opinion within the
scientific circle must be regarded as a healthy sign.
It is to the great body of scientists and engineers, more
than to any other group, that American industry,
and, therefore, America, owes its present position of
power. When scientists see mistakes being made in
scientific policy which must in the end endanger their
country, they should protest. In fairness, however, it
should be added that in matters of general politics
scientists all over the world do not seem to be less gul-
lible or more far-sighted than most other citizens.

The Position of Science

Americans believe in the power of technology to
change the world—as do the Russians. Industry is
pushing ahead vigorously, and enormous sums are

[1] The reader may wonder whether the Fuchs case has not made
nonsense of these statements. We must remember, however, that one
point brought out by this case is the extreme difficulty, if not impos-
sibility, of guarding against spies in high places. It is quite certain that
any system of control which aimed at complete and utter security
would kill off all scientific spirit in a very short time. Thus such a
system would do more damage to our efforts than that brought about
by possible enemy agents, grievous though this may be.

being devoted to research and development, much of which comes ultimately from Government sources. Thus we see everywhere lively activity in industrial research laboratories, staffed by large numbers of very able scientists and of engineers of the scientific type. They have the advantage over this country of being able to draw on their many excellent technical institutions, the Institutes of Technology, and the big engineering departments of their universities.

Apart from applied scientists and scientific engineers a large number of pure scientists work in the industrial laboratories and it was particularly interesting to find how many theoretical physicists are employed. This is a consequence of war-time experience, gained particularly in the atomic energy project, in which theoretical physicists played a very important role. They can be most useful in selecting the right type of experiment to be carried out from the large number of possible experiments, and in interpreting the results. There are also many problems which can be solved by pure reasoning, though it is true that this may involve very complicated mathematics. It may be instructive to quote the example of Euler, a Swiss mathematician, who lived about 200 years ago. At that time he designed a water turbine on purely theoretical reasoning. His design could not be tested at the time because technology had not progressed far enough, and later on it was forgotten. Last year a Swiss firm constructed a turbine exactly to Euler's specifications and found that it had an efficiency of over 70 per cent, a figure which has only recently been surpassed by modern machinery of comparable size.

A visit to an American industrial research laboratory generally presents a picture of an enthusiastic group of

able and well-trained people united in their aim to
increase man's power over nature and to make life
more worth living. Whether or no this aim is defeated
at the human level is another question. In any case,
America is now the leading industrial power of the
world. Although this in itself may not be alarming, it
is alarming indeed to see how American industry is
continuously becoming more and more powerful and
how this is happening at the expense of industry in the
weaker countries.

There are many reasons for this tendency. The first
is that wherever there is a high concentration of first-
class workers, they are bound to 'cross-fertilize' each
other, thus increasing still further the rate of advance.
An equally important reason is, of course, that prosperous organizations can offer better conditions of
work and better pay, and can also take more risks.
They can therefore attract the more enterprising
members of the weaker organizations, thus accentuating
further the disparity between the strong and the weak.

Here we should mention a more subtle point, but
one which is nevertheless very important—namely,
that strong countries are usually not troubled by
inferiority complexes. Let us consider what happened
in 1933, when a large number of scientists were
expelled from Central Europe, and particularly
Germany. One might have assumed that the scientifically weaker countries would have eagerly grasped this
opportunity of replenishing the ranks of their scientists
and engineers. However, what happened was just the
opposite; by far the majority of these refugees were
absorbed by the United States and Great Britain,
who were actually least in need of them. Scientists
in the scientifically weaker countries were reluctant

to give displaced scholars positions of importance, largely because they feared that people might think that they could not manage without them, whereas the States and the United Kingdom did not have this feeling of inferiority. The United States in particular took in very large numbers and in doing so profited considerably, especially in the now essential field of theoretical physics.

Are there then no weaknesses in the scientific set-up in the United States? There is one which is often emphasized by the Americans themselves. Americans have always been strongest in applied science, while for fundamental progress they have looked to Europe. There are, of course, historical reasons for this. That the same state of affairs still persists to a certain extent is perhaps mainly due to one reason: really good ideas do not come in the hustle and bustle of a very busy life. They come to people who have time to sit back and think. Life in America is, on the whole, not conducive to this, and in addition, the average American university teacher is often over-burdened with teaching. Some leaders of American industry believe that things will remain the same for a considerable time. In fact, one of them has actually suggested that most European scientists who settle in America are assimilated so quickly that they soon lose their specifically European qualities, and that America must therefore continue to depend on European scientists for fundamental ideas. America has, therefore, a direct interest in keeping European science in a healthy state.

While it is indeed true that in the past America has had to lean heavily on Europe for fundamental ideas, and still does to some extent, it seems to the writer that the importance of this point is often exaggerated in the States. There are now a number of organizations in America where scientists can work in a leisurely atmosphere and this, combined with the more favourable external conditions, has recently led to a strong development of fundamental science. Some of the most important new ideas have recently crossed the ocean from west to east.

It is, however, a very serious matter for Europe that their scientists increasingly want to settle in America. Many Americans realize this and K. T. Compton, the former president of the Massachusetts Institute of Technology, has given voice to their feelings: 'We should like to see foreign science restored to its pre-war vigour, not only in the interest of fundamental knowledge everywhere, upon which we and everyone can draw, but also because of the way in which a healthy body of science can contribute to economic and social recovery of all nations.'

This now leads us to the question: what can we do here in order to strengthen European industry? And then again to the wider question, whether any sort of equilibrium is possible between Europe on the one hand and America (and Russia) on the other.

This wider question is, of course, of a very complex and controversial nature, and in these matters purely political factors will tend to be decisive. However, we can try to discuss what the position is from the scientists' point of view. It seems an opinion often held, particularly in America, that if only one could bring European industry to the same high level of progress and efficiency as in America—and this should be possible if only Europeans behaved reasonably—everything would work out easily. But quite apart from the fact that the economic units are so much smaller in Europe, there are other important factors to be considered.

During a recent visit to France, it again became evident to the writer that this is particularly true of that country. A visit to any French laboratory will show why: the amount of money available for research is negligible even by European standards; salaries of scientific workers are so low that they cannot live properly on them, and many professors have to take on additional jobs.

Most important, perhaps, is that people do not seem to feel strongly about this. The French, in spite of all the scientific genius they have produced, are not primarily interested in science or in technology, as are the Americans—their real interests lie in the arts and literature. We have only to glance at the many book-shops to realize this. In France the working man reads really good literature, not the trash so prevalent in the States and increasingly prevalent in this country also. The French are probably the most cultured people in the world and (perhaps in consequence) they tend to be individualists and to dislike team work.

Team work, however, is necessary in modern experimental science and in its applications to industry, and in consequence the French have fallen back grievously in most scientific fields in spite of their many brilliant brains. Many French people, of course, realize this, but they seem somewhat resigned to the fact because it is the result of attitudes which are deeply ingrained, 'La vie est plus douce comme ça'— and they do, indeed, seem to live happier lives than much of the rest of the world. At the moment, at least, France cannot compete industrially in fields in which a scientific background is essential. We cannot discuss here the question of where in the hierarchy of world Powers France will eventually find herself, but it seems inevitable that she will have to step down politically.

THE LESSON FOR BRITAIN

Are we in this country going the same way as France, and losing, by default, our position as a world Power?

Admittedly, the British are a typically European people in many respects, and have a strong individualist tradition. But they have the advantage of being able to combine individualism with the requirements of working in a team. After all, it was this country which started the industrial revolution and set going all these recent developments.

Unfortunately, however, we have to recognize that political circumstances, and the short-sightedness of British industry during the past fifty years, have led to a steady falling back. That this need not have been so is quite obvious, since this country is second to none in scientific ability and technical skill. To see that this is still true we have only to consider our present lead in some specialized fields, such as that of jet-propelled aircraft.

The reasons for the relative decline of British industry were discussed in detail in a previous article. Let us now consider, in the light of more recent experience of conditions in America, what has to be done in order to make it possible for us to compete with America once again.

The writer's conviction is strengthened still further that the most important thing needed to make our industry competitive is the reform of technological education in this country. Neither our technical colleges nor the rather small engineering departments

attached to our universities can compete in quantity
or quality with the American Institutes of Technology,
or the large technological departments in their universities, which, in actual fact, are often so big and self-
contained that they are more or less equivalent to the
Institutes of Technology. What we need are institutes
like these, or the Zürich Technische Hochschule, if
we want to keep abreast.

These institutions can perhaps be best described by
the original statement regarding the four years' undergraduate course in science at the California Institute of
Technology. 'Its purpose will be to provide a college
education which, when followed by one or more years
of graduate study, will best train the creative type of
scientist or engineer so urgently needed in our educational, Governmental, and industrial development. . . .'
And later on: 'In all the departments of the institute
research is strongly emphasized, not only because of
the importance of contributing to the advancement of
science, and thus to the intellectual and material welfare
of mankind, but because research work adds vitality
to the educational work of the institute and develops
originality and creativeness in its students.'

Many prominent people are convinced of the need
for such institutes in Britain. Lord Cherwell, for
instance, has on various occasions stressed this point,
and so did Sir Henry Tizard in his presidential address
of 1949 to the British Association. However, obviously
nothing decisive has been done since, although time is
running out. The latest lukewarm report of the
Advisory Council on Scientific Policy is very disturb-
ing.[1] The main suggestion seems to be that existing

---

[1] A still worse report has already been referred to in a previous
article (page 16).

institutions should be improved (as, of course, they should), but the setting up of one or more new Institutes of Technology is obviously regarded as too big an undertaking. However, one really first-class Institute of Technology with the best people available, of whatever nationality (and certainly a number of foreigners would have to be engaged), might make all the difference and set a new standard. To get this going quickly would, of course, be a big undertaking, but we should not forget that the future of our industry is at stake. Let us hope that there are no inferiority complexes which prevent us from doing this.

One has to realize, however, that it is not enough to create such an organization, but that it must also have the full support of industry. Unfortunately one gets the impression that many industrialists are still not fully awake to this point. This is perhaps due to the fact that on the Boards of our companies we have still no proper representation of scientists or engineers. It should be mentioned, however, that in the past few years things have improved somewhat, and the writer knows of two cases in which scientists have invaded their Boards with outstanding success.

Another essential need is an improvement in the position of our scientists. Although working conditions at the universities are now on the whole satisfactory, salaries are still inadequate. Admittedly a step has recently been taken in the right direction, and the salaries of the younger scientists may not now seem too unsatisfactory in comparison with those of other people in this country, but they are still very much below what American industry—and even markedly below what American universities—can offer. The result is that many of the more ambitious young scientists and

D

engineers leave this country for America—a process which has now been going on for many years, and whose effects are only now being fully felt. Another effect of underpayment is that our scientists cannot work at full efficiency. There is little point in saying that now that we are going through bad times everyone must manage on less. If, for instance, a scientist wants to send his children to a university and he cannot afford to pay for it from his salary, he will either forgo his holidays, or he will take on additional work. Both must lead to a lowering of his efficiency for the job he is supposed to do, and that is just the thing we cannot afford.

This brings us to the more general problem of the distribution of money and goods to the population in times when there is not enough to go around. After all, only a small minority do the real thinking on which will depend our future. If, in times of scarcity, one cuts down all sections of the population in the same proportion one weakens also those who have to do the thinking for us—of course, not only the scientists—and by making them less efficient we sink still deeper into the mire.

The Russians do not suffer from this sentimentality. Their scientists are treated almost as well as their politicians. For instance, a member of the Russian Academy of Sciences gets seven times the food ration of the ordinary man, quite apart from the fact that he gets food of the best quality and does not have to queue for it! We have recently heard amused comments even from German university professors visiting this country, in comparing what they eat with what we get.

Many of our American friends who have visited

this country consider that the relative mental inactivity
here may be partly due to the fact that our diet contains
too much starchy stuff and too little protein. The writer
certainly felt more fit towards the end of his very
strenuous visit to America than at the beginning, and
it may be that the excellent food provided by the
generous hospitality of the Americans was partly
responsible for this.

The desire to be just to all can lead to defeating one's
own ends, and in America, for instance, a country in
which this desire is not a part of national policy in the
same way as it is in a welfare State, the great prosperity
has probably led to more equality in diet than in any
other country. There is really not much difference
between the diet of a cab driver and that of a company
director.

Another example of the way in which efficiency
suffers if the people who have to do the thinking are
not offered proper conditions: it is widely held that our
own atomic energy project is seriously handicapped
by its being run on Civil Service lines. The relatively
low salaries and the unavoidable 'red tape' keep out
many of the large number of high-class scientists, and
in particular high-class engineers, who are needed.
The ensuing waste of time and money is, of course,
incomparably more expensive than would be the
relatively small amounts of money which would be
needed to pay these top-class people properly.

Summing up, we see that American industry is
forging ahead at a rate with which at the moment
we are unable to keep pace. Whether this development
is going quite in the right direction is a different
matter, and one may doubt whether their whole set-up
would prove stable in case of adversity. This, quite

apart from all other reasons, should persuade us of the undesirability of attaching ourselves too firmly to the American band wagon and that we do not want to attach ourselves to Russia goes without saying. Whatever the ultimate outcome, a prosperous Britain is bound to be an asset to the world, and will be particularly important as a stabilizing influence during the next critical decades. But a prosperous Britain is only possible if our industry is developed to optimum efficiency. At the present time it certainly is not.

In this discussion only one particular aspect of the problem—though an essential one—has been considered. It may be that our politicians who have to consider the whole problem have come to the conclusion that, for other reasons, competition of our industry with that of America is out of the question. It may be that what they are doing is just the right thing, taking all aspects into consideration, and of course they have more data at their disposal than the ordinary man. Bearing in mind, however, our experiences between the wars, a scientist who has not yet recovered his confidence in the wisdom of politicians may be permitted to suggest that perhaps they simply do not know enough about these problems to realize their importance for our future.

WHY WASTE COAL?[1]

THE easy availability of power—or more correctly,
energy—is essential for our civilization. Without
it we could not run our factories or transport, nor
could we heat or light our homes. Energy, as man has
laboriously discovered, cannot be created—there is no
possibility of a perpetual motion machine—nor can
it be destroyed.

It can only be converted from one into another
of its many different forms, such as chemical, mechanical, electrical, or heat energy. We can draw up a
balance sheet for energy, and nothing that has not
been paid in can be taken out.

There are many different sources of energy from
which we can pay into our account, such as falling
water, wind, and fuels. The most important and, as
far as this country is concerned, practically the only
source is the chemical energy derived from the combustion of coal with the oxygen in the air; the figure of
about 200,000,000 tons of coal consumed annually
is now very familiar to everyone.

If all this potentially available chemical energy
could be converted with 100 per cent efficiency into
useful mechanical energy, every person in this country
would be able to have at his disposal fifteen horse power
at work for eight hours every day!

It is difficult to see where all this work goes to:
the suspicion arises that the work actually being done
for us is much less, and that the coal is being used
inefficiently. Let us consider the most familiar coal-

[1] *Financial Times*, June 2, 1948.

consuming machine, the steam locomotive. From this, heat leaks continuously and extravagantly, particularly with the escaping steam. Loud noises are emitted, which—although they themselves do not consume much energy—are always a sign of waste going on.

We shall therefore not be unduly surprised to learn that the efficiency of power conversion in the steam locomotive is about 5 per cent. The rest is lost as heat to the surroundings from these 'machines qui chauffent les champs,' as they have been called in France.

Would it be possible to design a locomotive to use the full 100 per cent of the chemical energy of combustion? In principle—yes. Chemical energy can in principle be converted directly into mechanical energy without the intermediary of heat, and in some chemical systems, such as the accumulator, this is done with nearly 100 per cent efficiency. However, for the only chemical source of energy of practical interest, the fuels, this problem has not yet been solved and there does not seem much prospect of its solution for many years.

For our purposes we have to distinguish between improvements which are possible in principle, but for which practical methods have not yet been worked out, and those which are fully developed and only waiting for application. The first case is not purely academic. Though quick returns are unlikely, we should certainly pursue research in this field. Enormous rewards would follow success. If the waste of fuel could be cut out from the process of converting chemical energy into mechanical or electrical energy, the production of chemicals, the metallurgical process, the supply of light and heat— assuming for the latter the ideal efficiency attainable with the 'heat pump'—in short, if all human activities requiring the use of power could be conducted without waste, then over 95 per cent of our coal could be saved. Fifteen 'horses' would no longer be required to do our work for us—one small pony would be enough.

While this forms the background against which we should view the whole problem, we are to-day mainly worried about our short-term difficulties, and this means that we must concentrate attention on the application of known remedies. Let us return to the example of the locomotive.

What could be done about this? Steam engines, although in many respects very suitable for use in traction, are not very efficient when built as small mobile units. On the other hand, a large modern steam-driven power plant has an efficiency of something like 25–30 per cent, and by electrification of the railways, the overall efficiency of a locomotive could be raised to about 20 per cent.

Another possibility would be to use diesel engines, which are even more efficient. Either of these alternatives would be difficult for this country at present; thus the electrification of the railways would require very heavy capital expenditure, while to be able to use diesel engines we should have to import large quantities of suitable fuel.

The energy consumed by the railways does not amount to very much in the energy balance sheet of the nation. But rather similar conditions exist in a number of other fields. If we could put into practice all the fuel-saving improvements which are already fully developed, we might save as much as half our coal.

These improvements are bound to come. How quickly this can happen in any particular case will, of course, depend in a complicated way on the economic situation, on the amount of capital expenditure involved, and on the degree of interference with normal operations which the particular change-over would entail. At the present time it seems unlikely that much can be done quickly to improve matters significantly in the industrial use of power, although efforts should be intensified in this direction.

There is, however, one field where a very large saving could be achieved almost at once. Our scanty coal supplies are being needlessly drained by the appallingly wasteful—and nevertheless ineffective—way in which we heat our houses. About 60 million tons of coal are used annually for domestic heating, and of this a very large fraction is burnt in open fires.

Now open fires have an efficiency of only about 15 per cent; they are 'contraptions to heat the stars,' as someone has said, and he might have added 'to soil the earth.' On the other hand, central heating installations are about 70 per cent efficient, and simple closed stoves about 40–50 per cent. Thus it should not be difficult to save, say, 20 million tons of coal each year simply by abandoning open fires, at the same time actually improving the general standard of domestic heating. If one considers the (really most efficient) way in which the open fireplace contaminates our houses and towns, there is an unanswerable case for the elimination of open fires as soon as possible.

The objections to this course are mainly sentimental; most people like open fires, just as small boys like the puffing noises and fumes of the old-fashioned locomotive. This love of squandering seems to be deeply rooted, but we *must* overcome it. The reward would be very significant. Twenty million tons more coal per year might change the whole outlook for this country.

The penalty if we fail could be severe; it might force upon us the most unpleasant way of saving—namely, going short of power and being compelled to sit in cold rooms.

We have no space to discuss here what should ultimately replace the open fire for domestic heating. It is clear that central heating must become increasingly important, particularly for large block heating systems, which should, if possible, use the 'off-steam' of power stations. Though central heating has not found much favour in this country, it is quickly accepted by most British people who experience it in other countries.

The whole problem is complicated by the fact that coal is not only a source of energy but also of valuable chemicals. This again brings in the question of the use of coke and gas. Some excellent reports have been written on these matters, dealing mainly with long-term policy.

However, what we need desperately is some quick and energetic action on the short-term problem. Even if it only provided a palliative this would be worth while, as long as no prohibitive capital investment was required, and the steps taken did not prejudice the application of the long-term remedies. In this field there is a curious lack of initiative.

The most effective step would probably be the quick abandonment of the open fire in favour of a simple closed stove, of a type which could be fitted in front of existing fireplaces. The required number of such stoves could be manufactured in, say, five years, without undue strain on the country's productive capacity, and could be provided at a cost of only a few pounds each. It is true that they would not look so attractive as open fires.

However, if the public were made to realize the benefits to the country, and to themselves, which would follow the general change-over to closed stoves, there is little doubt that the response would be good. Of course, the campaign would have to be handled intelligently. Too often when people are asked to save something, it simply means that they have to go short; it would have to be made quite clear that they would actually have warmer rooms by saving in this way.

An organization would probably have to be set up to look after the production and the prompt delivery and fitting of these stoves. Let us hope someone will have the initiative to do something in this vital matter.

The need to save coal has been forcibly impressed upon us by the shortage. If this shortage did not exist ought we still to go on squandering fuel and power as we did before the war? Surely not! Even if coal and other fuels were plentiful we would still have the problem of distributing excessive quantities of fuel and later having to get rid of the unused material and energy.

This latter is often a formidable job; very frequently the limiting factor in the design of machinery is the need to remove excess heat. In any case, the waste products, whether fumes, smoke, steam, or noise, are among the most unpleasant by-products of industrialization and every self-respecting community should try to keep its house clean—even if able to pay for the dirt.

ECONOMICAL HEAT PRODUCTION[1]

DURING the summer we are apt to forget about the seriousness of our fuel position. However, as soon as we have the first chilly nights and again hear Government announcements that electricity supplies will have to be cut during the winter, we are once more reminded that fuel economy is really the main pivot of our recovery. The one field where substantial saving could quickly be effected without causing hardship is in domestic heating.

However, the general public, which would be most directly affected by any measures taken in this matter, knows little about the fundamental principles involved in the generation and distribution of heat. Why is electric heating such an extravagance? What is this 'Heat Pump' about which so much has lately been heard and which is credited with saving enormous amounts of fuel? These and many other similar questions must be examined.

We remember, of course, that heat is a form of energy, and that energy can neither be created nor destroyed. How then can one method of producing heat be more efficient than another? True, heat is a form of energy like mechanical or electrical energy, and in the conversion of one form into the other, certain conversion factors operate, just like the rates of exchange between currencies.

A difference arises, however, from the fact that not all forms of energy can be completely converted into the other forms. This is forbidden by the laws of

[1] *Financial Times*, September 27, 28, 1948.

nature, just as the laws of England forbid us to change all our capital into foreign currency. The analogy fails in one respect: a process which contradicts a law of nature simply does not work, and this is definitely more than one can say of the laws of man!

One can easily convert mechanical energy into electrical energy with only small losses, or the other way round (by the dynamo or electric motor), and both of these forms of energy into heat (by mechanical friction or electrical 'friction' in an electrical resistance). But one cannot convert heat energy fully into either of the other two forms.

This is made painfully clear if we consider the efficiency of the conversion of heat from fuels into mechanical energy. Modern prime movers can have efficiencies up to 30 per cent, though on the average the machines at present installed in our power stations are only about 20 per cent efficient. Now we know that energy cannot be lost, so where does the rest go? It is given off as heat at the low temperature end of the process; this is what happens in the radiator of the motor car, or in the condensing towers of power stations, and there is no way of avoiding it. It is not due to faulty design, though of course this would make matters worse.

Fundamentally the reason for this onesidedness of nature is that heat consists of the disordered motion of the smallest particles of matter, the atoms and molecules, whereas other forms of energy are of an 'ordered' nature. It is easy to make disorder, and difficult to create order (not only in politics).

Let us consider as an example a motor car in motion. Its mechanical energy is made up of the energy of directed motion of all its particles. When one applies the brakes, this ordered motion is converted into the disordered motion of the particles which constitute the brake material.

To brake a car is quite easy, but we cannot use the heat temporarily accumulated in the brakes to start the car up again, although no energy has been lost! Thus there is an important difference between heat and the other forms of energy; those forms of energy like mechanical and electrical energy, which are freely and fully convertible into other forms, are called 'free' energy.

What determines the efficiency with which heat energy can be converted into free energy? These problems are studied in the science of thermo-dynamics, and the famous second law of thermo-dynamics gives the answer. We can produce free energy from heat only if heat 'falls' from a high temperature to a lower one. Thus we have to pay a premium for converting the disordered energy to the ordered form, and this premium is higher the lower the temperature difference at our disposal.

In all heat engines we supply heat (from fuels) at a high temperature, remove a certain proportion at a low temperature, and get the difference out as free energy. As the process becomes more efficient the higher the temperature difference, the designers of prime movers aim at higher and higher starting temperatures.

Now when we feel cold, we do not want free energy, but only this rather lowly, disordered form of energy, heat. We can obtain it in many ways, of which two are most important. The first is to burn the fuel in some suitable kind of closed stove or central heating boiler—generally situated in the premises to be heated. These have efficiencies up to about 70 per cent, the

rest of the heat leaving the house with the flue gases
(with more carefully designed stoves the efficiency
could still be increased considerably).

The other method is to use the most convenient form
of free energy, electrical energy, to produce the heat.
This can be done in very simple devices, electric fires
or radiators, and we get the full 100 per cent as heat.
But the essential point is that in order to produce the
electrical energy in the first place about five times—
and if we include distribution losses, six times—as much
heat energy must be used up in the power station.
Our overall efficiency is thus only about one-sixth; that
is, roughly the same as that of the open fireplace, which
is notorious for its inefficiency.

Electric heating of houses and water is very simple
and convenient, it is true, but from the point of view
of efficiency and economy it is indefensible. To have
encouraged it so much in the years before the war
was a serious error. At the present time, the extensive
use of electric heating does much harm to our national
economy, and is responsible for much of the overload
on our power stations.

Is there no way out of the difficulty which will still
make it possible to use the great advantage of electrical
energy—its easy distribution—without loss in economy?
This boils down to the question of whether there is some
way of getting a better 'rate of exchange' when converting the valuable free energy into heat.

For the answer we have to return to the heat engine.
Here we supply heat at a high temperature, extract
part of it at a low temperature, and gain the difference
as free energy. This we do in the steam engine by
evaporating a liquid at a high temperature, gaining
mechanical energy from the expansion of the steam,

and then condensing the steam at the low temperature, which means giving off heat.

Now there is no reason why we should not turn this machine the other way round. We would then evaporate a liquid at the low temperature end, taking up heat, and condense it at the high temperature end, giving off heat. Of course, we do not now gain free energy from the expansion of the gas, but have actually to compress the gas—that is, we have to supply free energy to a compressor.

This machine can be run in two ways: if we fix the 'high' temperature level at that of our surroundings and put the low temperature end into an isolated box, we have a machine that is familiar to everyone, the refrigerator. Heat is removed from the substances put into the box and rejected at normal temperature.

The other way is to shift the temperature levels towards higher temperature in such a way that we take up the heat at ambient temperatures, say from the water of a river, and deliver it at a somewhat higher temperature, say that which we would like to have in our rooms.

A device running on this principle is called a 'heat pump'; in design it is just the same as a refrigerator. Using a small amount of free energy we can remove heat from a lower temperature, and deliver its equivalent (plus that of the mechanical energy) at a higher level. We, so to speak, *pump* heat from a lower to a higher level. The amount of free energy consumed will depend on the temperature difference and be smaller, the smaller that difference. The factor which was against us in the conversion of disordered into ordered energy naturally acts in our favour in the reverse process.

With the average temperature conditions as they are

in this country, it can be shown (allowing for losses due to friction and other similar causes), that about five times as much heat can be delivered at the high temperature level in this way as would be obtained simply by letting the free energy deteriorate into heat, say in an electric fire. Of course, we do not create energy; the difference is taken up as heat from the surroundings and upgraded to a higher temperature.

Thus by making use of the heat pump we can get a better 'rate of exchange' in the conversion of free energy into heat. However, we have to pay a penalty. The machinery needed for this purpose is rather complicated and much more expensive than an ordinary closed stove. A heat pump installation for the average six-roomed house would probably cost £500–£800.

Now let us consider under what circumstances using a heat pump will pay. This depends mainly on the degree of availability of free energy in different countries. In England we first have to create our free energy using heat engines, from which we can only withdraw about one-sixth of the original energy.

With the heat pump we gain a factor of about 5, so that the heat finally delivered in our homes would be roughly 80–90 per cent of what an ideal stove could give us from the same amount of fuel; that is, somewhat higher than a good boiler for central heating. The small difference hardly makes this worth while in view of the higher capital expenditure.

In America, free energy is also mainly produced by heat engines, and thus the overall saving in fuel would again not be very high. However, one circumstance favours the heat pump over there; it can easily be designed in such a way as to make it possible to use it both for heating in winter and for cooling in summer.

This is, of course, a most attractive feature for the American climate, and the heat pump is bound to find a market among wealthy Americans.

The ideal field for heat pumps is a country which possesses a fair supply of free energy from water power, but has to import its fuel. Switzerland is such a country, and this, of course, is why the heat pump—the basic idea of which was put forward by Lord Kelvin about 100 years ago—was first developed there. Already a number of large buildings are heated in this way, the considerable saving in electrical energy counterbalancing the higher capital expenditure.

In Switzerland also the heat pump is used for industrial purposes. Obviously conditions will be more favourable in processes involving only small temperature differences, such as the evaporation of solutions (for example, in the sugar industry, and in the concentration of fruit juices). In this case the so-called 'vapour recompression' process, working on the heat pump principle, is used, and quite large plants are already in operation in Switzerland. It is of interest also that the plant used by the Americans during the war for the production of drinking water from sea water used the 'vapour recompression' system, as being the most economic in fuel consumption.

Even under the different conditions in this country, the use of the heat pump in the chemical industry would often be a practical proposition, and is definitely worth considering more seriously than has so far been done. However, we must leave this point for the present; much greater advantage to the national economy would in fact be expected if we could find a suitable way of improving the efficiency of domestic heating.

While the direct use of heat pumps for space heating

E

is not a very attractive proposition for us, the same thermodynamic principles may be applied in another way. We have seen that heat must be rejected from power plants. Ideally this should be done at the temperature of the surroundings; in practice, however, it is always done at somewhat higher temperatures because of difficulties in heat transfer. Now although this temperature is not high enough for use in domestic heating, one could alter the design of power plants so as to reject the heat at a somewhat higher temperature which would be suitable for use in space heating, by making use of 'back-pressure turbines.'

Of course, a little would be lost in the efficiency of the power plant, but the overall efficiency of such a combined plant is theoretically the same as that of a conventional power plant plus a heating plant working on the heat pump principle. In practice the combined plant would actually be somewhat more efficient because losses could be kept lower, and its capital cost would also be lower. The gain in efficiency of such a plant over an ordinary district central heating plant is, of course, even more marked.

There is no doubt that this technique would lead to the greatest saving of fuel and it should be considered very seriously in the planning of new housing estates. District heating plants, fed from the 'off-steam' of power stations, should be built wherever the geographical conditions permit.

However, the most urgent need is a solution of our short-term difficulties, and this seems to lie in the use of some type of installation which can be fitted in individual houses. Needless to say, we will have to abandon the open fire, which, apart from its prolific production of dirt, has an equally prolific consumption

of coal. Nor can we afford to use electric fires, since
their overall efficiency is just as bad as that of the open
fire, and, moreover, they draw on our scarce supplies
of free energy.

Let us assume that we could persuade half the people
to give up their open fires. What could we put in their
place? If we installed central heating of the ordinary
type, nearly 15 million tons of coal could be saved
yearly, but at the cost of a great capital expenditure—
of the order of £1,000 million. As a matter of interest,
it may be added that heat pump installations in the
same number of houses would save a few more million
tons of coal, but at a capital cost of probably at least
£3,000 million.

However, there is one simple remedy—the closed
stove. The wholesale replacement of open fires by
closed stoves of some simple type—even of as low
efficiency as 40–50 per cent—would give the greatest
possible saving of coal in proportion to capital expenditure. This would cost about £30 million and we
could then save about 10 million tons of coal per year.
Thus the cost could be recovered within a year!

These figures can only be rough estimates, but even
if they are wrong by quite substantial factors the moral
is clear. If we are really interested in balancing our
economy we cannot afford the doubtful luxury of
open fires. As has been pleaded in a previous article,
we must replace open fires by closed stoves!

An enterprising Government would offer free provision and installation of simple stoves suitable for
fitting in existing fireplaces. In this way they would
overcome some of the inertia and the sentimental
attachment of the public to open fires. There would be
no risk in such a project, and many much less profitable

projects involving the spending of public money have
already been started.

To sum up. We have seen that the heat pump can
effect appreciable savings in the conversion of free
energy into heat. This leads to very attractive possibilities for countries which can get much of their free
energy directly from water power, but is not so attractive for us who have to get it via heat.

Of course, the situation would change if we could
convert the chemical energy involved in the combustion
of our fuels directly into electrical energy, without the
intermediary of heat. This is possible in principle, but
it seems very doubtful whether a practical solution
to this difficult problem will be found within the next
fifty years, and for the time being we can exclude this
possibility.

We are sinners at a much lower level. We heat
our rooms mainly with open fires or electric fires,
thus wasting more than 80 per cent of the energy
quite unnecessarily. The only advantage which this
anachronistic relic of the days of plenty gives us, is
the possibility of improving our present situation easily
and quickly. So far, however, there are no signs of
even this modest effort.

PROSPECTS OF ATOMIC POWER [1]

A T present we derive by far the greatest part of our power from the chemical energy of fuels. Now the material of which the earth is made does not really provide us with suitable substances for these chemical reactions. Nearly all those reactions which can happen have already happened during the period of formation and early history of the earth which is more or less 'burnt out.' The stores of fuel from which we now draw are the remains of former life, minute in comparison with the rest of the earth and of course strictly limited.

It is, therefore, no wonder that when in 1945 the news broke that nuclear energy, or 'atomic energy' as it is best known, could be tapped, hopes were raised that all our power troubles would soon be overcome. People were led to believe that atomic energy would soon be the determining factor in the well-being of nations, and at present the real or simulated desire for atomic energy is one of the important factors in relations between countries.

To understand the actual position we have to say a few words about the basic physical facts. Every atom consists of a heavy nucleus which has a positive electric charge and a number of electrons surrounding the nucleus in the form of a cloud to give an equal negative charge. The chemical properties of the atom are determined by this electron cloud so that each element is characterized by the magnitude of the positive charge of the nucleus. This nucleus was regarded for

[1] *Financial Times*, December 7, 1948.

some time as an entity remaining unchanged in all reactions, chemical or otherwise. What happens during chemical reactions is that rearrangement of the electron clouds takes place, resulting in the formation or dissociation of chemical compounds.

At the beginning of the century the phenomena of radio-activity were discovered and these finally led to the discovery that the nucleus itself was not an unchangeable unit but could be split up into smaller parts and we now know that these parts are the so-called protons which are positively charged and the neutrons which have no charge. All nuclei consist of different combinations of these two units and it was soon found that nuclei of the same element—that is, with the same charge—could be built up in different ways and with different masses. The different types of atom which can make up a given chemical element are called isotopes of that element.

The reason why the nucleus generally behaves as an indivisible unit is that the energies required to make these changes are very much higher than those connected with chemical changes—actually about a million times higher. With the development of methods for producing very fast particles, of which the cyclotron is the best known, and particularly with the discovery of the neutron, and of methods of producing and handling these particles, a whole 'nuclear chemistry' has developed during the last few years. Atoms are 'transmuted' by reactions affecting their nuclei. In a way these are analogous to the ordinary chemical reactions of the electron cloud, but they differ in character and the energies involved are about a million times greater. The same power can be produced by 'burning' about a millionth of the weight necessary with the ordinary chemical reaction. In addition, since at first sight it appears that any amount of nuclear fuel is available, compared with the strictly limited stocks of chemical fuel, prospects would seem to be very bright.

Actually the sun itself gets its energy from a nuclear reaction, the combination of hydrogen atoms to form helium. Combination does not take place directly, but through a very complicated cycle, the so-called 'carbon cycle.' Even at the temperature of the interior of the sun, however (about 25 million degrees), one cycle takes 5 million years.

Tapping of nuclear energy by means of the fission of the uranium isotope 235 which forms somewhat less than 1 per cent of the natural uranium is a very much simpler process than the building up of helium from hydrogen. Of course, very much less of the material required is available and there are several other important difficulties. For instance, in the 'piles' in which the process of nuclear fission is maintained as a chain reaction (during which the new fissile element 'plutonium' is formed) the energy is developed in the form of heat and so far no direct way of utilizing nuclear energy is in view. When heat has to be used as intermediary in the production of power from fuels it is necessary to use high temperatures in order to extract the power efficiently. During the war there was no time for such developments and the energy was simply run to waste; now, however, efforts are concentrated on this problem. Serious technical difficulties have to be overcome. There is no doubt that they will be overcome, though it may be a few decades before a satisfactory machine is developed.

When this is achieved, how can the energy be used most advantageously? First, it is necessary to realize that nuclear reactors have to have, for technical reasons, a certain minimum size, and if ordinary uranium is the raw material this is quite formidable. By using uranium already concentrated in the isotope 235 the size can be considerably reduced, but it is still impossible to dispense with the very heavy radiation shields necessary for protection. This probably means that the main application of nuclear fuels will be for large power plants, and it is quite certain that such small units as would be required for motor cars cannot be produced.

There has been much speculation about the cost of nuclear power and much has been said about the coming 'atomic age,' when power will be had for the asking. However, the initial cost of fuel is usually less than one-sixth of what the consumer has to pay for his power—the rest going to pay for generation, distribution, and services. Thus even if nuclear fuel costs nothing—and it certainly will not—there cannot be any spectacular changes in the cost of power.

Of course, this argument cuts both ways; if nuclear fuel turns out to be much more expensive than coal it would still not affect the final price very considerably. Present estimates, which can only be very rough indeed, suggest that nuclear power might cost about the same as the power obtained from coal. Nuclear power will certainly be most valuable for certain specialized purposes; obviously it will be a particularly attractive proposition for all purposes where the light weight of fuel is important, such as the propulsion of liners or perhaps the irrigation of deserts.

However, the question of whether nuclear power will be able to satisfy an important proportion of our world power needs depends ultimately on the availability of the fissile materials. So far, uranium is absolutely essential and thorium can be used as an auxiliary 'fuel.' Neither element is very rare, but there are few deposits of really concentrated material. If we have to depend on known deposits of this type nuclear power will not be able to play an effective part in providing for the world's power needs.

The position may change, however, if one of the two following possibilities proves feasible. First, it may be possible to work up the deposits of very poor ores in a reasonably economic way. Secondly, it may be possible to use, not only the uranium 235, but also the isotope 238, which is more than a hundred times as abundant as the 235. This depends on the number of new nuclei of plutonium which can be made (from 238 nuclei) per fission. If this figure is greater than unity one can, so to speak, 'breed' new fissile material and thus use up all the uranium. The chances of successful breeding are not yet known with certainty, but one thing is clear: even if it is possible, the building up of sufficiently large stores for any practical use will take a very long time, say thirty to fifty years.

Let us assume for purposes of argument that in one way or another we find enough fissile material to provide a large part of the world's power supplies. If the cost is roughly the same, what will be its advantages over coal? As has already been mentioned, there is the special attraction for some purposes arising from the fact that only a very small amount of fuel is needed—particularly the reduced need for transport. Another advantage is that the unpleasantness of the mining operation itself may be largely avoided. (The situation may of course be different if we have to rely on poor ores, and from what one hears about large labour forces chasing after rather small amounts of ore in the mines in Saxony, it does not seem too promising.)

But we must not forget that an atomic energy plant is a singularly unpleasant type of plant—quite apart from the misuse to which the products can be put. It is true that in a normally running pile the radiation hazard can be made very small. The working parts of the plant, however, become highly radioactive so that if some repair is needed one cannot approach the plant at once, but it has first to 'cool' down for many months. Further, a very essential part of every atomic power plant is the chemical plant required to deal with the highly radioactive products; this is most difficult to work since it can only be operated from a distance. Finally, a very tricky problem indeed is the question of disposal of the radioactive fission products. For a single pile or even a few dozen this would not be too difficult, but if any appreciable part of the world's power consumption had to be provided by atomic energy it would be a most serious problem.

Thus, summing up the prospects of atomic power, one can say that it may prove very useful for some types of specialized projects. Whether it can ever contribute an appreciable part of our total power remains to be seen, but this will certainly not happen within the next fifty years or so. Thus, for a long time to come we will have to rely on coal as our basic source of power; the possibility of plentiful atomic energy in the distant future must in no circumstances be allowed to deflect us in our attempts to improve the output of coal.

Of course we must not forget that there are other important applications of nuclear energy apart from the production of power, some of which will be discussed in a later article.

POWER SOURCES OF THE FUTURE[1]

WHAT will happen when our fuels, which have so far supplied most of the power we need, are eventually exhausted? It is true that coal in this country will last—at the present rate of consumption—for at least another 100 years and for the world as a whole for at least ten times longer. Also, natural gas and oil from oil shales can considerably extend our dwindling oil supplies, and petrol can, of course, always be provided by the hydrogenation of coal. The time is bound to come, however, when our strictly limited supplies of fuel are exhausted. So we must begin to look around for other sources of power. We must not forget also that mining is an unpleasant operation—this fact is actually mainly responsible for the present shortage—and other sources might perhaps supply the necessary power in a more agreeable way.

First, a word about the cost of power. On the whole, one can say that the cost of fuel and power is not very important in national economy. In this country, for instance, it is less than 5 per cent of the national income. A better illustration perhaps is that we spend less on this item than on either tobacco or drink!

We must have power, but, within limits, the price does not affect our economy very much. If the cost of power all over the world doubled, or even trebled, it is not likely that our standard of living would be affected to any great extent. Large differences between the costs of power in various countries are another matter, although we should not exaggerate their importance.

[1] *Financial Times*, January 14, 1949.

69

Norway, for instance, has abundant cheap power, while Switzerland is short of it. This has not knocked out Switzerland or made Norway prosperous. Many other features determine prosperity, and the result in this case has only been that Norwegian industry concentrates on processes needing a great deal of power and Switzerland on high-quality products.

Now will we ever be unable to get our necessary power even at a price?

This question can be disposed of with one sentence. The world power consumption at present corresponds to about 2,000 million tons of coal per year—an amount of energy which the earth intercepts from the sun's radiation in six minutes! We are actually showered with power and have so far relied mainly on fuels because of their high concentration of energy and the relative ease with which they can be tapped. Let us now consider the possible alternatives to fuel as sources of power.

Water power—30 per cent of the sun's radiation falling on the earth is used for lifting water, but only a very small part indeed of this water arrives at such a position that it can be used for the generation of power. Water power is, of course, a highly convenient form of energy and its main disadvantage is the great capital expenditure required for the plant. All countries with potential sources of water power are already developing them as quickly as permitted by their economies. But water power can never be the full answer to the world's power needs, in particular because it is concentrated in relatively few places.

Wind power—About 2 per cent of the sun's radiation is converted into kinetic energy of the air, which thus represents a considerable store of energy. Wind power is used in small installations at isolated positions with success. The necessity for large structures, however, makes it unsuitable for use in the large-scale production of power; moreover, the supply of wind is so irregular that we would be in a grim position indeed if forced to rely on it.

Tidal power also represents a considerable store of energy, but only at a few places would utilization be possible and it certainly cannot replace coal to any great extent. The Severn Barrage scheme has been seriously considered in this country, and the estimate has been made that with a capital expenditure of £50 million we could save annually about a million tons of coal. But, with the same capital expenditure devoted to improving our heating appliances, twenty times as much coal could be saved. Tidal power is obviously therefore not an attractive proposition at the present time.

Another project which has received considerable publicity lately is a French suggestion that temperature differences in the ocean could be used. A plant for 3,000 kilowatts is said to be under construction. Even for this power, however, the installation becomes so bulky that one can hold but little hope for this project.

The sun's radiation—All the power sources discussed so far, with the exception of tidal power, derive their energy from the sun. Why is so little effort put into attempts to utilize the sun's energy directly? First, let us consider the orders of magnitude. Let us assume that we could retain one-tenth of the energy falling on the outer atmosphere after losses due to reflection, absorption (including bad weather), and the change of intensity due to the changing angle of incidence.

Let us assume further that we can utilize 10 per cent of the energy arriving in the converting mechanism. Then a total area of the size of Egypt would be sufficient to supply power for the whole world. This shows that the project certainly has great potentialities, but also that very large areas will have to be covered with the converting mechanisms; they must therefore be very simple and cheap.

Most of the attempts so far have used large mirrors to concentrate the radiation on boilers, and, of course, these have to be turned according to the direction of the incident sunlight. This kind of installation is much too expensive for large-scale use, though modern developments in mirrors of aluminium foil might change the picture.

A better solution would be the use of cheap photo-electric cells, which might have efficiencies of power conversion of the order 5–10 per cent, and there is no reason why such cells should not be developed. Photo-chemical reactions have also to be considered. Perhaps the simplest solution would be to grow plants, and afterwards burn these under boilers; in this connection it is quite encouraging to see that the cost of using cane sugar as a fuel would be (at present prices) only about ten times as high as that of coal. The difficulty in plantations of this kind is in the provision of an adequate supply of water since so much is lost by evaporation from the plants.

However, plans are now being considered for the building of very cheap greenhouses from plastic material which would permit the circulation of a restricted amount of water within the system. This is also an interesting proposition for food production. Incidentally, attempts to use the power from the sun and to grow more food would naturally compete with each other, but the areas potentially available are so large that one need not fear a clash.

Direct power from the sun will certainly not be used on any large scale within, say, the next fifty years. However, it seems to be one of the most promising possibilities for the more distant future and may supersede fuels—either because these become exhausted, or even earlier because they involve such unpleasant occupations as mining.

It is known that the Russians are very active in developing this source of power and that a certain amount of work is also going on in America. Unfortunately, nothing seems to be going on in the British Commonwealth.

The prospects of *atomic power* have been discussed in a previous article, in which it was shown that there is a possibility that it might at some later time be able to take over from conventional fuels, although this is by no means a certainty. It goes without saying that both solar and atomic power should be developed vigorously and this should actually be happening at the present time, even if for no other reason than that one of these might eventually provide a more pleasant way of tapping power than by digging in the bowels of the earth.

But why the general public puts so much hope in atomic energy and 'cold-shoulders' the sun is a mystery—perhaps the sun has not quite the glamour of atomic energy. But after all the sun is nothing else than a nuclear reactor and there is the definite advantage that it is at a safe distance, free for all, and out of reach of politicians.

The present power shortage is in many ways similar

to the shortage of food. In both cases there are potentially enough sources to supply adequately at least the present world population, and with possible future developments (such as the synthesis of food or the use of solar power), to supply a greatly increased population.

The dangerous period is the present and near future since in neither case can production be increased quickly, particularly in the prevailing political atmosphere. As has recently been pointed out, the food situation may well become catastrophic before it can be improved.

However, there is one important difference between the two shortages: we cannot do much about better utilization of food, the body looks after this more or less automatically, and actually with very high efficiency. But we can do a lot about the better utilization of power. As has been shown in previous articles, we only utilize a few per cent of the power consumed, the rest going to waste.

By a modest effort we could save enough to make us secure against crippling power shortages. By a determined effort we could save about half of the present consumption; that is, about 100 million tons of coal per year in this country alone! This is the only reasonable and safe way to deal with the power question before new sources of power come into action.

WANTED: A NATIONAL FUEL POLICY[1]

ONCE more we have a coal crisis. Why is this? The essential facts are quite simple. Practically the only source of power in this country is coal. Coal mining is such an unattractive occupation that the number of miners is falling steadily and this offsets the effect of improvements due to mechanization. There is no chance that we shall much exceed the present annual coal output of 200–220 million tons in the near future.

On the other hand, we are faced with the absolute necessity of providing more power for our factories, if we want to work with the efficiency needed to compete for world markets. (American workers use two to three times as much electricity *per capita* as their British counterparts.) This means that we must increase our electricity output within the next two or three decades by at least a factor of 3 which corresponds to an additional coal consumption at the power stations of perhaps 50 million tons per year.

Where is all this power going to come from? From atomic energy? There is not the slightest possibility that we shall get significant amounts from this or any other new source during, say, the next twenty years. We must realize that for some time to come we shall have to make do with the present rate of coal production, so the additional power we need must be found by using less somewhere else. The failure to realize this is responsible for the present situation and matters

[1] *Financial Times*, December 8, 1950, and January 5, 17, 1951.

will get progressively worse unless a realistic fuel policy is adopted by the Government.

But what can be done? In earlier articles I have explained in some detail how we are actually using only a small percentage of the energy contained in the coal while the rest is being allowed to go to waste. Of course, not all this wasted energy could be saved without new developments, but about half could be saved if only we applied properly our existing knowledge. About half of this again could be salvaged by methods not involving great capital expenditure.

One simple way of reducing the wastage is by improving domestic heating, which takes about one-quarter of all our power. The open fire has an efficiency of only about 15 per cent, quite apart from being a prolific producer of smoke and dirt. But little is yet being done to introduce central heating or stoves in new houses—still less to replace open fires in existing houses, say, by simple closed stoves.

An equally bad offender is electric heating. Here the loss does not take place in the house but at the power station, which only converts a small part of the energy, say a fifth, into electricity. In a way, electric heating is worse than the open fire as it also uses up power station capacity of which we are woefully short. Of course, it is legitimate to use electricity for occasional heating in, say, bedrooms and bathrooms, but to use it as a main source of heat is inexcusable and should be most strongly discouraged.

We see, however, that the policy of the former electricity companies of encouraging the use of electricity, is still being continued. But if everyone were to switch over to electric heating we should just about have to treble the generating capacity of our power stations.

The greater part of the energy supplied to the power stations is carried away as low-grade heat which is of no use to anyone. Now by running the turbines with a somewhat higher exhaust temperature we could, at the expense of a relatively small reduction in their efficiency, obtain the rejected heat at a temperature which would make it suitable for the district heating of houses. Plants of this kind would, of course, be a little more expensive to install than ordinary types of central heating, but from the point of view of the economy of the whole country they would be extremely desirable as they would make possible the saving every year of many million tons of coal, which could then be fed into more stations supplying power to industry.

All this is, of course, well known and many reports have been written about it by scientists and engineers. Why then is nothing being done about it? Even if the wasteful methods of heating had the advantages ascribed to them, the fact remains that they are a luxury which we cannot now afford and in which, incidentally, no other nation indulges. There are always plenty of excuses possible for doing nothing, but one wonders what kind of miracle the Government is expecting to get us out of our present difficulties.

Political and economic problems are generally so complex that it is seldom possible to grasp them in their entirety, and most politicians have to rely on the method of 'muddling through.' This may be all we can hope for in politics, but it is a very poor way of approaching questions which are essentially scientific. Scientists usually view their problems as a whole and they generally seem to do so in a detached and open-minded manner. It is therefore imperative that they should be able to exert their influence on technical policy.

During the war this was common practice, but it now seems that policy decisions are once more reserved for politicians, or at least for people with a classical or legal education. Is another catastrophe needed before scientists are given their proper part in managing this 'age of science'?

It is high time for drastic steps to give effect to a National Fuel Policy designed to make the best combined use of coal, gas, and electricity. Surely this was one of the benefits to be derived from nationalization! Of course, nobody likes controls, but in a crowded industrialized world some directives are unavoidable. The essential point is that we want to retain our intellectual freedom, but we may be well on the way to losing it if, by happy-go-lucky methods, we undermine the economic foundations of the country.

IMMEDIATE MEASURES

Let us now consider what ought to be done at once. The best hope of a quick return is in the field of domestic heating, which at present consumes roughly one-quarter of our coal output.

By ensuring an efficient use of the fuels and by cutting down draughts and improving the thermal insulation of houses, about two-thirds of this coal could be saved. Unfortunately, the most efficient method of domestic heating—district heating using the heat rejected from power stations—can only be a long-term development.

There are, however, two ways open to us of getting quick results. The first is to reverse completely the present policy of encouraging electrical heating. Now the protagonists of electrical space-heating point out:

(*a*) That power stations burn inferior coal which cannot be used otherwise. This is partly true, but quite irrelevant. No one suggests that less electricity should be produced—actually we urgently need much *more* electricity for productive purposes in industry.

(*b*) That it is much better to transport coal in large amounts to power stations than in small lots to individual houses. This is of course true, but we should have to transport three times as much coal to the power stations as to houses with proper heating appliances.

(*c*) The heating load is a desirable load as one can store heat at off-peak times. The great majority of electrical heating appliances are, however, the radiators which are offered in such profusion in the shops, and these cannot store heat. A glance at the load curve shows that ~~domestic~~ heating accounts for ~~about~~ half

ERRATUM

Page 79, line 19, should read :

shows that electric heating accounts for up to a third

much too precious to squander when less valuable forms of energy would do. It is like feeding bread to cattle when there is not enough to go round for human consumption.

The second way open to us of getting quick results is to do away with another luxury—and a very doubtful one at that—the open fire. The immediate reaction to this suggestion is usually the rather stereotyped reply that the Englishman's life would not be worth living without open fires—at least, the lives of those Englishmen who do not have to carry the coal themselves. The reply is, however, likely to be quite different if we ask the same question of an English housewife, who has to keep her house clean, or of anyone who thinks a bit further and is ashamed of the grimy appearance of our towns.

Neither is this love of open fires shared by Englishmen who have experience of central heating or of stoves in other countries. We must also realize that in giving up open fires we would also to a large extent be giving up draughts. It is quite possible to reduce the draught in the average English house to about half, without getting a stuffy atmosphere, and this in itself makes a very considerable additional saving.

The question of the necessary administrative action is not primarily the scientists' concern. As, however, there have not been any really effective suggestions so far, let me venture to step into the breach.

1. All schemes involving electricity as the main source of heating should be stopped at once. Since it would not be possible to destroy existing electrical heating appliances, penalizing tariffs should be introduced for all electricity used above a fixed limit based on the legitimate needs of the consumer.

2. Two years ago I formulated the following scheme for the abolition of open fires:

'The immediate abolition of open fires would, in my opinion, be the greatest and easiest step towards economic recovery. They could be replaced by simple stoves designed to fit into existing fireplaces. I believe the Government could not spend any money more profitably than by offering to provide and install such stoves free of charge. If only half the owners of fireplaces accepted this offer about 10–15 million tons of coal could be saved each year at a capital expenditure which, if the enterprise were organized properly, could not be more than £30 million.'

The cost of such a scheme, which, of course, would cover all those people forced to give up electric heating, would be recovered within a year or so. It should not be too difficult to carry out the whole project within a few years.

If there was not sufficient response and there were still people who would prefer to import American coal in order to continue their anachronistic heating methods, even at the expense of sacrificing the economic future of their country—then I am afraid drastic measures would have to be taken. Instead of cutting supplies to industry, only so much coal should be allocated to each household as would be needed if proper heating methods were employed.

There are, of course, many people who are against any kind of planning and believe that, given complete freedom to do what one likes, everything settles itself for the best. These anarchists always remind me of the sanguine citizen who informed H.M. Inspector of Taxes that after careful consideration of his proposals he had decided not to join the income-tax scheme.

Apart from quick-return measures, long-range measures should, of course, be started as well. Special

attention should be given to the proper planning of
heating in new settlements, especially to methods of
district heating, and to the better utilization of coal in
industrial processes, to pumped storage schemes and
the storage of steam on a large scale—to mention only
a few of the more important possibilities.

It should not need emphasis that in planning the
proper utilization of our fuels on a national scale,
what matters is not whether one particular scheme is
economical on its own merits but from the point of
view of the economy of the whole country.

Such planning should therefore be at Government
level and should be the foremost duty of the Ministry
of Fuel and Power. There is not the slightest doubt
that if proper action were taken, savings could be
effected which would provide the 10 or 20 million
tons of coal per year which we need now and the
fifty or sixty which we shall need twenty or thirty
years hence—and this without our going short.

It seems obvious to me, as I have already said,
that the scientific point of view should be strongly
represented in this planning. Unfortunately most
people have hardly any scientific education and this
perhaps applies particularly to the strata from which
politicians are drawn. As one of our few scientific
peers recently remarked in the House of Lords: 'I am
sure if the ordinary scientist knew as little about history
and literature as the ordinary arts man knows about
science, he would be certified and locked up within a
fortnight.'

It is therefore all the more necessary to have scientists
or scientifically educated engineers in high-level
administrative positions. Long experience has shown
that to have scientific advisers only is not good enough

—it is too easy to disregard their advice if one does not like it.

Scientists should be essential ingredients of administrative bodies—incidentally, this should also be true of industry—not only because of the knowledge they can offer, but also because they can contribute the 'operational research' approach which proved so valuable in the most diverse fields during the war. The scientist's independent attitude and way of thinking cannot be dispensed with when, as I hope, we at last embark upon a fuel policy on a national basis.

I personally cannot help feeling that if scientists had in the past been allowed their full share of responsibility in this matter, the present critical situation would not have arisen.

SOME OBJECTIONS ANSWERED

I have tried to impress on the reader the absurdity of the situation in which we find ourselves because we have no fuel policy. The lack of 5 or 10 million tons of coal may mean disaster to us even though with our present knowledge we could reduce our waste of coal by about 100 million tons per year.

I have also indicated what, in my opinion, should be done to deal with the situation, and in particular suggested some measures concerning domestic heating which would yield quick returns. The response in correspondence to the Editor and to myself has been vigorous, not to say violent.

I now want to sum up and to deal with some criticisms of these suggestions which have been made. Some are based on trivial misunderstandings, probably arising from the fact that in short articles one cannot go into much detail. For instance, I have been accused of trying to deprive out-of-the-way places of the benefits of the modern electric cooker. Of course this was not my intention. I maintain, however, that in towns where both gas and electricity are available it is indefensible for the electricity authorities to persuade people to change from gas to electric cookers.

The main criticism has been directed against my suggestion that the Government should provide stoves, free of charge, to fit into existing fireplaces. This is, of course, not an ideal solution and is only intended as an emergency measure to effect a quick saving of coal. If we want quick returns, it is obvious that we must do something about *existing* houses and not only think about better solutions for houses not yet built.

As 60 million tons of coal per year are used for domestic heating (either directly or in the form of gas and electricity) at an average efficiency of under 20 per cent, very large savings must be possible. Nevertheless, it has been suggested by some critics that while the installation of stoves would increase comfort in the house, there would be no saving. In reply I would point out that in pre-war Germany, for instance, where houses were much better heated through longer and harder winters than we have in this country, the coal consumption per person for heating was only 60 per cent of what it is in this country.

As my plan envisages the provision of a stove only for each of those rooms where there is now an open fire in use, it should be possible to improve on the German figures and at the same time to provide increased comfort. The amount of coal which could be saved if such stoves were generally introduced should

be between 20 and 30 million tons of coal per year;
it is of little importance whether one believes the upper
or lower figure to be more realistic.

What does matter is the capital investment involved
in any such scheme. I indicated that for an investment
of £2–£3, one ton of coal could be saved per year.
Perhaps this estimate is a little optimistic—I had not
corrected the figures for the change in value of the
pound since I first made my proposition some two years
ago. However, let us assume for the sake of argument
that the figure might be as high as £5. Even this would
mean that the capital outlay could be recovered
within two years.

In order to save 20 million tons of coal per year
£100 million would have to be invested, and this is,
of course, a very large sum. To gain the right perspec-
tive, however, let us look at other comparable figures.
For instance, some years ago the Severn Barrage
scheme for tidal power was seriously discussed and
still has its protagonists. At the present price level it
could not be realized for less than £100 million,
and the saving expected is only 1 million tons of coal
per year. For the same expenditure the return is
one-twentieth that which would be produced by the
stove plan!

One correspondent has rightly pointed out that
£200–£300 million are now invested in generating
and supply equipment to provide electricity for space
heating. And all this money was spent only to make
heating a little more convenient—without any saving
of coal. If the present mistaken policy of encouraging
electric heating by granting unrealistic rates is continued, many times these sums will have to be
invested.

Some correspondents are indignant about the suggestion that the Government should pay for the stoves. May I first remind these critics that the money invested in power stations and coal mines is also public money. It is all-important to cut out unnecessary coal consumption as quickly and at as low cost to the nation as possible. If this can be done only by spending public money—and I believe that most people would not be able to pay for the stoves out of their own pockets—then such spending would be in the national interest.

The most violent attacks have been made by people who regard such a scheme as an infringement of their freedom. Actually I put forward the plan as an optional one and only added that in case of insufficient response it might be necessary to cut coal supplies to the householder to a level which would ensure comfort only if proper heating appliances were used.

Very probably no need for this would arise. A survey made by the Egerton Committee shows that 34 per cent of the people questioned were in favour of central heating, 45 per cent indifferent, and only 21 per cent preferred open fires. Although the choice was not directly between open fires and stoves it is clear that the supposed hold of the open fire on the British public is greatly exaggerated.

Nevertheless, the point raised by these correspondents involves an important principle. One of them states emphatically that it is purely his own business how efficiently or inefficiently he heats his home. Does he realize that his primitive ideas about freedom rob the country of about 100 tons of coal during his lifetime; that he pours many hundredweights of soot and dirt on other people's heads and houses; and that his extravagance condemns one miner to labour quite unnecessarily for about three months?

Does he realize that at present about 100,000 miners are doing nothing else but labouring for the coal needed in excess of what would be sufficient if proper heating methods were applied?

Mining is obviously an unpleasant job which no one is very anxious to do and we have no right to demand that people mine coal which is then only wasted. So far, attempts to deal with the situation have been directed towards getting more coal—probably because the proper course of reducing waste calls for more imagination. The present policy has certainly not been conspicuous by its success. Is it not high time that we settle down to evolve a National Fuel Policy designed to make the best and most economical use of our coal for the benefit of the whole country?

ATOMIC ENERGY[1]

SHORTLY before the war experiments in Germany, Great Britain, and France had shown that the uranium isotope 235 could be split under neutron bombardment, and the possibility of a self-propagating chain reaction soon emerged, which could lead to an enormous development of energy by small amounts of separated uranium 235. However, existing quantitative data were insufficient to determine with certainty whether this was possible.

At the beginning of the war a number of scientists in this country realized that this was a matter of the greatest importance, not only because it might provide a decisive weapon for us but also because it might do so for the enemy. Experiments carried out under great pressure soon established that the bomb was a real possibility and other experiments showed that it should be practicable to separate the required isotope in sufficient amounts in time, although this would certainly be a major undertaking. In 1941 the British Government decided that the matter was of sufficient importance to warrant large-scale developments.

The matter had, of course, also received attention in the United States, but no really serious development had been initiated. In November, 1941, a mission of American scientists visited this country. Their report that we, though at the time in desperate straits, had begun a large-scale effort, 'triggered' the American project which then developed into the enormous and successful undertaking about which we all know.

[1] *Financial Times*, December 9, 1948

Close co-operation was established between the two
countries, and it was soon decided to transfer a number
of British scientists to the States in order to work on a
combined effort in that country. It was realized that
the chances of success would be improved in this way
because of America's much higher industrial potential
and freedom from bombing.

What can be told about these developments is laid
down in the official American document, the famous
'Smyth Report,' which is still more or less the 'Bible' of
this subject and in which the implied 'Thou shalt nots'
are as important as the information divulged. It was
obviously written—in haste—mainly to justify before
the American public the enormous expenditure of
money and manpower on the project. This explains
some of its weaknesses.

One of these is that practically all the developments
are credited to citizens of the U.S.A. This is perhaps
not very important as British scientists are not primarily
concerned with 'priorities' or 'credits.' Another weak-
ness is more serious. What can be told and what can
not? It was—the writer believes rightly—laid down
as a main principle that the fundamental physical
facts could be divulged; these could in any case have
been rediscovered very quickly by scientists in any
country and there is no secret 'formula' which can be
handed over to an enemy. The real secrets are
technical matters. How does one separate the isotopes? Which method is the quickest to put into
operation? How does one purify the pile materials?
How does one deal with the highly radioactive fission
products? And scores of similar problems.

The compromises reached in the Smyth Report
are often inconsistent. Driven by the understandable

desire to show the American public what difficulties had to be overcome and how many different methods had to be followed up, much information has been given away of a kind which must enable any country starting afresh in this field to save two or three years, whereas on minor points information is often obviously and deliberately withheld. One can perhaps best describe the kind of compromise which has been reached by the story about the man who visits his friend on a Sunday morning and finds him clothed with nothing but a top hat. Asked what is the matter he replies: 'Well, I didn't expect anyone to come on Sunday morning.' 'But why then the top hat?' 'Oh, one never knows, someone might turn up after all.'

But even with the knowledge gained from the Smyth Report and subsequent publications, the practical release of atomic energy is still bound to take many years for any country which did not take part in the wartime projects. This is partly because nothing is said in the report about the construction of the weapon itself, but mainly because of the time needed to acquire the technical 'know-how' in the field of isotope separation and for the production of plutonium in piles. The question in everyone's mind at present is: How long will it take the Russians to produce bombs? It is true that they have a number of first-class scientists and engineers; they are masters of improvisation and will certainly make a very determined effort.

However, two factors are against them. An atomic energy project has to draw on technical experience in very many fields which is easily available only in countries with high technical development throughout. The second and perhaps even more important point is that novel developments of this kind can only thrive

in countries where the best scientists and engineers
are able to come to the top and are at liberty to follow
the lines which they think most promising, without
fear of being 'liquidated' in case of a setback or a
political conflict. This is made abundantly clear to
anyone who compares developments in America and
England with those in Germany, as vividly described
in Professor Goudsmit's book, *Alsos*.

Until recently scientists in Soviet Russia were held
in higher esteem and had more freedom than the
scientists of Nazi Germany. But now this distinction
between the two régimes seems to be disappearing.
Recently many of Russia's best geneticists have been
purged because the theories of the charlatan Lysenko
appeared to fit better into the current Soviet political
ideology. It has just been reported that Russia's
foremost theoretical physicist has been 'warned' by the
party and the latest rumours are that the quantum
theory itself is in disgrace as its famous 'principle of
uncertainty' does not fit into the ideology. We need
not complain about this. If it comes to a fight between
party and quantum theory it is quite clear which
will survive in the end.

On all the evidence it seems a reasonable estimate
that Russia cannot have the first bomb in less than,
say, another three years and probably not before five
years; moreover, one bomb is, of course, of no military
value. To produce enough to 'saturate' an enemy
would require many more years.[1] The energy released

[1] As is well known, the Russians have obtained the atomic bomb
a few years earlier than was generally expected. The main reason for
this seems to be the underestimate that was made of the effectiveness of
Russian espionage activities which has now been disclosed by the Fuchs
case and others. It is now clear that very important information was

G

by the bomb is stated to be that of 20,000 tons of T.N.T. The destructive power is, however, somewhat smaller, as the area at the centre of the explosion is 'over-pulverized' and its effective equivalent in T.N.T. is estimated to be 2–5,000 tons. Perhaps at first the importance of the weapon was somewhat overrated. If one considers, however, that this destructive power can be carried by a single aircraft, that 'improvements' are very likely to have been made, and that the production of a cloud of highly radioactive material adds to the effect of the weapon, it is clear that the atomic bomb must dominate military thinking as well as the thoughts of potential victims.[1]

So far all attempts to obtain agreement on a plan for the effective international control of atomic energy have failed. This matter of control would, in principle, be very much simpler if it were possible to make a clear-cut division between the production of weapons

available to the Russians which must have saved them a considerable amount of time and effort.

Another reason seems to be that the picture of suppressed science given in the article is not entirely correct. Later information seems to indicate that in actual fact the majority of scientists are more or less free to do as they like if only they pay lip service to the official doctrines. From time to time, one discipline may be singled out for a reprimand in order to impress on the scientists that they must not go too far in their disregard of the official line. These purges are seldom allowed to go so far as to interrupt too seriously experimental work and scientific progress. For instance, while all official teaching in genetics now follows strictly the Michurin-Lysenko line, the majority of experiments are planned without any regard for it at all.

It is known that all the more important publications of Western science are very quickly translated and circulated to Russian scientists by an excellent organization. Also, contrary to the impression given by the official Soviet propaganda, Russian scientists have the highest regard for Western science and very quickly assimilate its results into their own work.

[1] New developments seem to indicate that the later types of 'conventional' bombs have a considerably higher efficiency. The so-called hydrogen bomb, which so far has not yet been produced, would be again orders of magnitudes more powerful.

and the production of power. Unfortunately this is not the case. The large reactors which are envisaged for the production of power at the same time produce plutonium, which can replace the uranium 235 as material for the bomb. For a short time it was believed that by using 'denatured' fissile material it would be possible to obtain the power without at the same time producing material which could be used in a bomb. This hope, however, seems to have been over-optimistic.

A third application of atomic energy lies in the use as research tools of reactors or the materials produced by them. Nuclear reactors or 'piles' contain very high densities of neutrons. These can, for instance, be used to influence chemical reactions—a very promising field—but their main use is in the field of nuclear physics itself. Intense neutron beams emerging from piles have already proved to be a most powerful research tool for investigating the structures of atomic nuclei.

Of more general importance is the use which can be made of substances formed in the piles either spontaneously or by design, and which are radioactive isotopes of ordinary elements. As we have seen, the properties of such isotopes which depend on the 'electron cloud' structure—that is, all chemical properties and most physical properties—are practically identical with those of the ordinary element. But we have nevertheless a method by which the radioactive isotope can be detected even when mixed with the ordinary non-radioactive isotope—observing it by its radioactivity. We can thus use these substances, so to speak, as 'spies,' who can mix unrecognized with the crowd (the non-radioactive isotopes) but can nevertheless get in touch with us and report where they are. In this way we can get information on biological or chemical reactions which are very difficult to elucidate in any other way. For instance, if we feed an animal with a quantity of a foodstuff of which a number of the molecules contain atoms of a radioactive isotope, we can 'follow' these molecules anywhere in the body. Important progress has already been made by this use of 'tracer' elements in the kinetics of biological and chemical reactions.

Another application lies in medical therapy. Some elements are preferentially attracted to particular parts of the body; for instance, iodine by the thyroid gland. By feeding a food containing a radioactive isotope of iodine we can expose the thyroid gland to localized radiation—which may be necessary for the treatment of a malignant growth.

The quantities of these radioactive 'tracers' needed for research purposes are quite small and can be provided by piles of low power, which cannot produce the larger amounts of plutonium required for bombs. The establishments of the American project and our own Harwell are already able to satisfy all reasonable demands.

Only large industrial countries can muster the means necessary for developments in the military and power fields. One cannot help feeling that at present many countries have a desire for the weapon which is camouflaged—consciously or unconsciously—by a professed desire for the benefits of atomic energy, and enormous sums are now being spent by the major Powers on this project. Even the smaller of the industrialized countries are also trying to take part in these developments. For these countries attempts to develop more than the purely scientific aspects will probably lead to waste of money and scientific manpower which can ill be afforded.

To sum up.   If we weigh the potential benefits of atomic energy in power production (discussed in a previous article) and in research, against the potential dangers, it is obvious that with the present standards of international morality we would be happier without it. Some people have suggested a moratorium on the development of nuclear physics for the next fifty years, to allow political morals to catch up with the progress of science. This is, of course, not a realistic proposal, and in any case the damage has already been done. We have to try to make the best of a bad job—as with so many other things.

ISOTOPES IN INDUSTRY[1]

THE extensive work that has been and is being done on atomic energy has led to an abundant supply of isotopes. These give us a new tool which, though still in the early stages of exploitation, is being increasingly used in science and industry. One can foresee that it will play a great part in future industrial research, and it is therefore intended to deal with it in some detail.

In order to understand what isotopes are, we must begin by recalling that all substances are made up of minute units, called atoms, combined together in small groups called molecules. Until about fifty years ago it was considered that atoms were the final indivisible units, and that all the atoms of one element were exactly alike—there was no way of distinguishing one from another. We now know, however, that the atoms are made up of many particles; they consist of a heavy nucleus which has a positive electric charge and a number of electrons in the form of an encircling cloud carrying an equal negative charge. It is this electron cloud which alone determines most of the ordinary properties of the atoms, including their chemical properties.

It has also been shown that the nucleus of the atom, whose charge determines the size and structure of the electron cloud and therefore its chemical properties, is not a final indivisible entity. The study of radioactive properties of matter has proved that the nucleus also is made up from many smaller particles—

[1] *Financial Times*, April 25, 26, 1950.

neutrons and protons—which may be grouped together in different proportions. By combining different numbers of uncharged neutrons with charged protons, nuclei with the same charge but with different masses may be built up. This means that there are atoms with the same electron cloud—that is, with identical chemical properties—but with different nuclear structure; they are called isotopes and generally have a different weight and sometimes a different radioactive behaviour. It was soon found that the great majority of natural chemical elements consist of a few stable isotopic species, which so far as we are aware have been present ever since the elements were created.

Thus it is no longer true to say that all the atoms of a chemical species are alike. We may suppose that all the atoms of a chemical element wear, so to speak, the same uniform (or electron cloud) which determines their behaviour in all normal actions. Inside, however, they are not alike: spies, or nuclei, of a different nature may lie hidden under cover of the same uniform. To use these spies is the essence of the application of isotopes.

To take an example, we may smuggle spies of an isotope of nitrogen among the normal nitrogen atoms in a fertiliser. Then, if a plant is fed with the fertiliser, the nitrogen atoms make their way into it. Although there were already many nitrogen atoms in the plant we can find out which have come from the fertiliser because these will be accompanied by the spy isotopes which we can recognize by their nuclear properties.

To make use of these stable isotopes we have first to obtain them, then install them as spies in the process we want to investigate, and finally to locate them. They are obtained by separation from normal elements by methods which are simple in principle, but very cumbersome in practice. (In order to obtain comparatively small amounts of one particular uranium isotope for their bomb project the Americans had to build vast factories covering many hundreds of acres.) Though very small quantities indeed are sufficient for tracer work, much time and effort is still needed to produce them. In order to distinguish between the spies and the normal atoms we must weigh the isotopes; the most sensitive and direct way of doing this is by using an apparatus known as a mass spectrograph. This, though complicated, is well known to physicists and will, no doubt, soon be on the commercial market.

The stable forms of isotopes were used before the war, especially in biological work, but they are both expensive to obtain and difficult to detect, so their use was, and still is, rather restricted. The great increase in the use of isotopes follows the discovery that we can make artificial ones by exposing normal atoms to high-speed particles created in one of the familiar accelerators, such as the cyclotron or, better, in an atomic pile. An element is thus transmuted into an isotope either of itself or of a chemically different element.

This is a very much simpler way of producing our spies. Also since most of the isotopes created in this way are unstable and thus radioactive, it makes it very much simpler to find out where they are. We need no longer weigh the atoms but can detect them by their radioactivity—that is, by the radiations they produce. The spies, so to speak, have wireless sets and can get into touch with us directly. There exist special instruments which are extremely sensitive to the radiations, so that only very small amounts of isotopes are needed for our intelligence service. Two of the best known of these instruments are the Geiger counter and the photographic plate. A counter can detect even as little as one ten thousand-millionth of an ounce of radioactive material.

As radioactive isotopes are so much easier to lay hands on, and as they are so much easier to detect, they now dominate the field almost completely. However, stable isotopes are still used either when the radiations might do damage, as in some biological work, or when no convenient radioactive isotope is available—as in the case of such important elements as nitrogen and oxygen.

The best way to show the many different uses to which radioactive isotopes can be put, is to discuss a few characteristic examples. Their medical applications are given first, as this was where they were originally used.

Their most important medical use covers investigations into the workings of the body. To take a simple case: we often want to know how quickly certain substances (say, common salt) are taken up by the body and where they are finally absorbed. We prepare a salt solution containing a little radioactive salt so that it is detectable with a counter but quite harmless to drink. By applying counters to various parts of the body we are able to see where and when the salt is absorbed. There are many variations of this type of experiment, by making drugs, vitamins, and medicines containing radio-elements. By 'tagging' food we can find where that, too, is absorbed: this may indicate an abnormality associated with some disease.

Now a few industrial examples. In metallurgy, isotopes offer a means of investigating properties of materials and of experimenting with new alloys. For example, the amount of phosphorus in steel is crucial; even very small concentrations make it dangerously brittle; their detection and quantitative measurement is very difficult except by isotope technique, when the great sensitivity of the counter measures them easily. By tagging the atoms of one component of an alloy with an isotope, it is possible to see whether that component is spread evenly throughout the metal after casting, for if not, different sections of the cast will give off different amounts of radiation.

The same technique may be used to study deformation in a metal. It should be possible to introduce into a continuously cast billet of metal a layer or slice containing radioactive isotopes which would normally lie in a flat slice. If, after processes such as forging or extrusion, deformation had occurred, this slice would be no longer flat and would be detectable by examining the new positions of the isotopes.

The chemical industry is one which offers great opportunities for the new isotope technique. By tagging one component in a chemical process with isotopes it is possible to trace the movement of that component through the whole process, to see what happens to it, to see how it is divided up among the resulting products, perhaps to see how much is left as waste on the walls of the vessel.

An analogy, used recently in a Harwell report, may make this clearer. Imagine a chemical process between colourless liquids taking place in glass vessels. How much more we would know about it if one of the components could be coloured. We could see it entering the first vessel, diffusing into it, and then travelling through the whole process, sometimes going this way, sometimes that, sometimes dividing into two or more parts. Further, if we could colour each component in turn we could gain much insight into the way the reaction worked. But this is just what isotopes enable us to do.

Industrial processes, for the most part, take place in large vats or stills which are generally made of steel, and it is hard to follow the progress of the reactions except by frequent and tedious analysis of the contents of every stage. Now suppose that one of the constituents is tagged with radioactive isotopes before entering the process. Then, at any time, in any vessel, the presence of this constituent may be detected by its effect on a counter. Moreover, the relative amount is also measurable; the more of it the greater the indication on the counter. Thus in all the complex processes, including adsorption, desorption, and distillation in which one component is separated from another, we observe what is happening easily and directly.

This applies, for instance, to the chemistry of refining, to the production of synthetic petrol from coal and gas, and to the complicated processes of polymerization which play such large parts in the production of chemicals from oil. There are also obvious applications to microchemistry—a branch of chemistry which deals with reactions between substances of which only very minute quantities are available.

Isotopes can help us also in industrial health problems. Mercury vapour is a cumulative poison, and even very small amounts in the atmosphere will injure the health of workers breathing it for a period of years. Thus in factories using mercury it is important to check that the atmosphere is free of the vapour, but this is very difficult to do by traditional methods because of the minute quantities of mercury involved. However, if liquid mercury is made radioactive, any vapour from this liquid will also be radioactive and may be readily detected by the counter.

Other general industrial problems to be studied include the flow behaviour of gases in furnace flues by introducing isotopes into the hot gas.

The efficiency of fog filters has been checked by making the fog particles radioactive and then seeing if the filter removes the activity. The obscure nature of the part played by sulphur in the vulcanization of rubber has been investigated, as has the adhesion of ice to rubbery materials, this last providing valuable data for the de-icing of aircraft.

Obviously, once a process has been investigated by the isotope technique, the same technique may be used to control or monitor the process on an industrial scale. As an interesting example we may mention the problem of coating rayon fibres, only ·004 inch in diameter, with a layer of sodium oleate prior to being dyed. Since the quality of the dyeing depends on the thickness of the coat, it is most important to keep this uniform.

By using radioactive sodium in the sodium oleate, the reading of a counter near to the coated thread gives a continuous indication of how much activity and therefore what thickness of coating has been put on the thread. The radiation from an isotope decreases with the passage of time—in some cases practically no more radiation is given off after a few minutes, while in others the radiation continues almost unchanged for hundreds of years. Hence by choosing an isotope that only emits radiation for a few hours, we can ensure that the final rayon product will be quite free of radio-activity.

So far we have considered how isotopes may play

the role of spies or tracers. Apart from all this they may in some cases be used as a cheap source of radiation in place of X-rays or radium.

The power of radium to destroy cancerous tissue has long been known. It has the advantage over X-ray treatment that the pellet of radium may be placed right by the growth, thus reducing the ill effects of the radiation on adjacent healthy tissue. The disadvantage of this treatment lies in the small amounts of radium available. But now radioactive isotopes, which are just as effective, are available at a fraction of the cost.

There are many other applications for it as a source: we may use it in certain cases to take X-ray pictures without a cumbersome X-ray tube. We may use the power that the rays have of ionizing gases to make the air conducting and so dissipate dangerous static electricity produced in such processes as sand-blasting.

We may measure the thickness of a given piece of material by noting the reading of a counter when the material is placed between it and a calibrated radioactive isotope. This gives a continuous and accurate reading of thickness varying from that of soap films to sheet steel. A variation of this technique enables one to find the thickness of a pipe by purely external measurements.

In order to clean out oil pipelines a screw plug is inserted at one end of the line and is carried along by the flow of oil, turning and cleaning as it goes. Sometimes it sticks somewhere in the pipe and then the pipe has to be cut open to get it out. But where does one make the cut? Obviously if the screw carries a radio isotope the answer is simple—one rides along the pipeline until the counter gives an indication, then there

is the screw. Or again, the bores of oil wells are sometimes lined with cement, the depth of which is difficult
to measure. If the cement contains a radio isotope
and a counter is lowered down the bore a ready
indication of the depth of the cement is easily obtained.

Even this short account shows the great number of
fields in which isotopes have been used, although
we have only been able to obtain them readily during
the past four years.

How then is industry to take full advantage of the
new developments? Primarily it is for the industrial
scientist to decide which of his problems can be dealt
with by the new technique. Industrial firms have or
should have research departments capable of deciding
how this new technique could help them. For the most
part, however, they will be ignorant of its details.
Their men will have to take short training courses
in the methods of handling and detecting isotopes;
the methods are simple and they will soon learn how
to conduct the experiments themselves.

The equipment required is comparatively cheap.
We may expect that many firms will begin production
of this equipment for the commercial market, as is
already being done in America on a large scale.

To help small firms which only wish to use the
technique occasionally and cannot afford the staff and
equipment, it is likely that special firms of consultants
will be set up to meet their needs. These would give
advice on how isotopes may be used to solve particular
problems, and would help in carrying out the actual
experiments.

For bulk supplies of isotopes we must rely on atomic
piles, and in all countries these are or will be controlled
by the respective Governments. The atomic establish-

ments of America and of this country distribute isotopes for research purposes at moderate cost, and our Harwell pile has up to the present been able to fulfil all the requirements of this country and most of Europe. Actually, only small piles are really needed to provide materials for isotope research, and so this peaceful application of atomic energy is an unmixed blessing. Power piles, on the other hand, have to be much larger and produce dangerous amounts of plutonium, so that their eventual appearance must be regarded with mixed feeling.

It now remains for industry to make full use of these new opportunities, and perhaps for applications of a more domestic nature to be evolved. The first step in this latter direction was possibly taken by a visiting American professor, who was reduced to living and feeding in a boarding-house in this country. Being of a suspicious nature he tagged the leavings on his dinner plate one day with radio-isotopes. At the end of the week 'shepherd's pie' appeared on the menu; unfortunately for the landlady, however, it loudly proclaimed its origin to the professor's counter. Even if this story were not true it could well have been.

OXYGEN IN INDUSTRY[1]

OXYGEN is chemically a very reactive element—that is, it has a great tendency to enter into chemical combination. Very many substances are thus found in nature in the form of oxides. Materials which have not yet undergone their reaction with oxygen can on account of this 'affinity' be used to provide us with energy, and are the so-called natural fuels, coal, oil, and natural gas. (To the fuels we should add foodstuffs, which, though not found ready-made in nature, are continually built up by plants with the help of sunlight.)

Fuels are used mainly for two purposes—to provide us with energy or to produce the high temperatures required in many metallurgical and chemical processes.

We know that it is a difficult matter to find enough fuel, and usually take the other side of the reaction, the oxygen, for granted. Generally, we only have to see that air has free access to the reacting system. But air consists of oxygen only to the extent of about one part in five, the rest being nitrogen—apart from about 1 per cent made up of a mixture of rare gases. Thus we actually use the oxygen only in a very dilute form.

There are a number of advantages in using pure oxygen:

1. We can attain higher temperatures in the burning of fuels because we do not have to heat up the useless nitrogen during the reaction.

[1] *Financial Times*, February 9, 1949.

2. We gain in efficiency as the nitrogen normally carries away much of the heat produced.

3. The combustion chamber can generally be smaller, for similar reasons, or a given apparatus can have an increased output.

4. In chemical processes the use of oxygen often leads to the production of material of higher quality, if nitrogen has undesirable effects, or inhibits the desired reaction.

Up to the present the use of oxygen has been mainly restricted to applications where high temperatures are essential, as, for instance, in cutting and welding. Whether it is likely to be used on a large scale in industrial processes will depend, essentially, on the price. It is clear that we will have to pay for the separation of the oxygen from the air, but it can easily be shown that an ideal process would do this very cheaply— the energy required to separate 1,000 cubic feet would be only about 2 kw.h. Thus, in principle, cheap oxygen is a possibility.

Formerly, chemical methods were used for oxygen production, but proved much too expensive. Modern oxygen technique started when a physical method was introduced, that of distillation. If one heats a mixture of two constituents having different boiling points, the constituent with the lower boiling point evaporates preferentially. Although this does not achieve complete separation, this becomes possible if we repeat the process and make it continuous. This is done in distillation columns, so well known from their use in the alcohol-water separation, and in the separation of crude oil into its various constituents.

Now oxygen and nitrogen are gases at room temperature and they become liquid only at very low tempera-

H

tures—about two-thirds of the way down to absolute zero, the lowest temperature possible—nitrogen having a somewhat lower boiling temperature than oxygen. Thus these gases can be separated by distillation if they are first liquefied, provided the whole system is sufficiently well insulated to prevent undue heat influx from its surroundings.

This insulation is actually quite a simple matter, particularly in large units, and the feasibility of the process then depends on finding a good method for the liquefaction of air and on designing very efficient heat-exchangers. Modern liquefaction techniques are all developments of the original methods of Linde, in Germany, or Claude, in France. Compressed air is expanded either through a nozzle or in a so-called 'expansion engine' and this produces a cooling effect which, by the use of heat-exchangers, is made regenerative until finally liquid is produced.

The combined efforts of physicists and engineers have resulted in a very high efficiency in the oxygen separation, and the most modern plant, which uses expansion turbines and improved heat-exchangers, has a power consumption of only about five to six times the theoretical minimum. The total cost of oxygen will, among other things, depend on the cost of power, the question of continuity of demand, and, of course, on the purity required.

The very pure (about 99·8 per cent) gas which is needed for cutting and welding is more expensive than gas of 90–98 per cent purity which is adequate for many purposes, and oxygen of lower purity is still cheaper. Very large plants should be able to produce medium-purity oxygen for less than 2s. per 1,000 cubic feet. To the cost of production we usually have to add, however, the considerable cost of transport. We cannot, of course, transport oxygen at atmospheric pressure as it would be much too bulky.

One possibility is to compress the gas to a much smaller volume and to transport it in high-pressure cylinders. The pressure used in practice is about 120 atms. The great disadvantage of this method is the heavy weight of the high-pressure cylinder, which is about ten times that of the gas it contains.

In the last twenty years, therefore, another method has gained much ground, that of transporting oxygen as a liquid. The density of the liquid is about 1,000 times that of the gas at atmospheric pressure, and no heavy container is required. Of course, the vessel has to be thermally insulated to prevent undue losses during the short time of transport, a relatively simple matter. The liquid is then evaporated at the place of consumption. The large lorries which transport liquid oxygen, with their typical spherical containers, have become quite a familiar sight.

Both methods are, however, too expensive for really large amounts of the gas, 'tonnage oxygen' as it is called. Really cheap oxygen in large amounts for industrial uses can only be provided by an oxygen separation plant on site. This, of course, means heavy capital investment, so that very careful consideration has to be given to any proposal for the replacement of air by oxygen in a large-scale process.

Let us now consider the main applications for large-scale use of oxygen. It is evident that we are not interested in it for power production except, perhaps, for very special machines such as rockets. It is true that the efficiency of thermal prime movers increases with the temperature at which the heat is supplied, but they cannot yet make full use even of the temperatures attainable with air.

The main potential use of 'tonnage' oxygen is in metallurgy, particularly in the production of iron and steel. Iron is usually found in nature as oxide, and in order to prepare the pure metal one has to bring the ore into contact with carbon—generally as coke—which has a higher affinity for oxygen and combines with it, thus setting the iron free. This reaction is rapid only at high temperatures, and it is carried out in the well-known 'blast furnaces.'

The product still has too much carbon content for normal use and this has to be reduced and other impurities removed before a good steel can be produced. This is done either in the 'Bessemer converter,' or in the 'open hearth furnace'—alternative methods for the same purpose. In this part of the process hot air is blown either through or across the surface of molten crude iron.

It is possible that the use of oxygen in all three processes will be found to lead to economy and higher yield, although the question is very complex and depends on local conditions, since the exact methods used differ from one firm to another. The oxygen required need not be particularly pure and can be the so-called 'medium-purity' or 'tonnage' oxygen.

In the blast furnace the advantages of using oxygen are rather uncertain as the temperatures required here are not very high. In the open hearth furnace, however, the use of oxygen greatly increases the output of a given furnace and at the same time reduces the consumption of fuel.

It has been claimed that the output can be increased by as much as 40 per cent with a reduction of fuel consumption of one-quarter. In view of the extensive use of the open hearth process in this country this seems to be the most promising possibility for short-term improvement. In the Bessemer converter the use of oxygen improves the quality of the steel since the nitrogen absorbed by the molten metal from the air is believed to be harmful. In the same way, the use of oxygen in the small-scale manufacture of special alloys is advantageous.

Another important application of oxygen in industry is in the production of petrol from natural gas, a process which has been developed recently in America. The method is based on the well-known Fischer-Tropsch process, which uses carbon monoxide and hydrogen as raw materials, and these can be obtained by the oxidation of methane from natural gas.

A large plant is being erected in Texas for this purpose and will require a production of oxygen nearly as great as the whole present output in the United States. The use of oxygen in the gas industry may also be useful; it is believed this will lead to greater flexibility in operation. Combinations of these two processes seem especially promising.

In general we may say that revolutionary changes in the near future arising from the more extended use of oxygen are unlikely, and long-term development will be necessary in many fields. In the long run, however, oxygen will certainly play an important part in industry.

We can end on an optimistic note. The importance of oxygen is now being realized in this country, although in the past our oxygen industry lagged behind Germany and France in methods of production and behind the U.S.A. and Russia in the development of applications.

Since the war vigorous interest has been developed in these problems. New research departments of the oxygen industry have been built up, which, together with the British Iron and Steel Research Association, are working in close contact with the branches of industry most concerned.

ELECTRONIC BRAINS[1]

THERE has recently been a considerable growth of scientific literature dealing with 'automatic computers,' 'electronic brains,' and similar devices. Parallel with this, a new vocabulary has appeared containing such words as 'negative feed back,' 'servo-control,' and, most impressive of all, 'Cybernetics.' These outward and visible signs signify a development of first-rank importance and at least one notable scientist regards these developments as likely to be more far-reaching in its effect on our civilization than even the much-discussed atomic energy.

We are all, in fact, familiar with simple types of automatic computers such as cash registers or office adding machines. Ever since the abacus man has used devices to help him in performing calculations. In recent years, however, and particularly during the past twenty years, the range and scope of these aids has been extended tremendously, so that even very complex mathematical problems can now be handled.

Two main types of calculator can now be recognized: these are known as analogue computers and digital computers. In the former, one may say that the calculation of a particular physical problem is carried out rapidly by setting up in miniature in the machine a copy of the problem. The slide rule, familiar to many, is a basic example of such a computer, the actual lengths set up on the slide being directly related to the numbers or quantities under consideration.

[1] *Financial Times*, August, 16, 17 and 18, 1950.
This article is a co-operative effort of Dr. D. K. C. MacDonald and the author.

Again, the automatic anti-aircraft predictors used in the last war were essentially analogue computers; the speed of an aeroplane might be represented by the amount of an electric current flowing in some part of the circuit, its rate of ascent or descent by the amount of another current elsewhere, or possibly by the physical rotation of a cam. The appropriate deflection to be applied to the gun—that is, the solution of the problem—would then appear, perhaps, as the amount of rotation of a pointer (on an electrical instrument). Machines of this type can work very rapidly, but are naturally not very flexible because they are only designed to deal with some specific class of problem. Furthermore, as is obvious in the case of the slide rule, the accuracy is directly limited by the accuracy with which the individual parts of the machine can be made.

In the digital computer, however, with which we are more concerned here, the essential feature is that a particular complex calculation is broken up into a large number of very simple basic operations—essentially addition or subtraction—each one of which can be dealt with by a relatively simple, standardized, and easily replaceable electrical valve circuit. However, because of the extreme rapidity with which electric valves can operate—generally in periods of the order of one-millionth of a second—a calculation may be carried through in a matter of seconds or hours where days or even many lifetimes would be needed by a human brain. Moreover, the accuracy is now limited only by the number of units which we are prepared to incorporate.

It may at first sight appear impossible that an abstruse mathematical equation can be split up into such elementary operations. We have, however, to recall that multiplication, for example, is really only a repeated process of addition which ultimately we memorize. Thus, while we say 'by experience' that $5 \times 2 = 10$, a machine of this type would probably carry out the operation $2 + 2 + 2 + 2 + 2$. The principle can be extended to cover essentially all the complicated operations of mathematics, because these are all ultimately based on the elementary processes of addition and subtraction, multiplication and division.

In general terms, a computing machine can cope with two classes of problems. On the one hand it might deal with a direct question, such as $53694 \cdot 32 \times 81213 \cdot 11 \div \cdot 01635$, or, 'What is the charge for 33 gross of grub-screws at $3\frac{1}{4}d.$ each and 100 dozen nuts at $2\frac{1}{2}d.$?' —to each of which the answer might well be given in a fraction of a second. It is immediately obvious that such a machine could effect an enormous reduction of time and labour in bookkeeping, for example, but it is still of the same family as the common office calculator, even though, of course, the increase in speed may be spectacular.

The more significant fact from the point of view of the future progress is that machines of this class are capable of handling problems of the following kind: 'What is the most economic schedule to give an express train from A to B allowing for such factors as the cost of fuel (which increases with speed of the train), the number of trains which can be run (which improves with the speed of the train), the wages bill, and so on?' This question, although itself a relatively simple example, is typical of the kind of problem which has to be tackled in every field of science, production, economics, and even psychology, and can be dealt with by the machine because it can carry through a vast number of trial solutions of the problem in very quick succession until the best is achieved.

It is evident that some control has to be incorporated to make sure that successive attempts at a solution tend progressively towards improving the result and not in the opposite direction. Let us consider finding the square root of 10. As a first trial, let us say, we start with 2; we then multiply 2 by itself, obtaining 4. If then we try again with 3 it is evident that we are now closer to the correct answer (in fact, 3·16) than if we had chosen 1 as our second trial.

In such a problem the automatic control required would have the task of comparing successively the difference between 10 and the square of 2 (that is, $10 - 4 = 6$) and between 10 and the square of 3 (that is, $10 - 9 = 1$). So long as this difference continues to diminish we know we are moving towards the correct answer (thus $10 - (3 \cdot 1)^2 = 0 \cdot 39$). If, however, it changes sign ($10 - 4^2 = -6$) we know we have overshot the mark, and must retrace our steps. Similarly, in the problem of the express train schedule we must 'instruct' the machine to compare successive trials at a solution until minimum cost is obtained—that is to say, until any other solution tried would lead to a higher cost than the one chosen.

It is the incorporation of such automatic controls which enables a machine to direct its own operations in dealing with problems of this kind. This vital feature is a type of 'automatic error correction' or 'negative feed-back' and is at the heart of the great advance which has been made with these machines and with 'servo-control systems' which can be used, for example, in conjunction with a predictor, to control automatically the position of a heavy gun.

A homely example of negative feed-back arises in the way one rides a bicycle. It appears that the speed of a bicycle is generally too low for there to be appreciable gyroscopic action of the wheels in keeping us upright. What happens is that we observe constantly simply the difference between our position and that of the vertical, and correct this continuously by adjustments of the handlebars. Similarly, an automatic steam-engine governor, designed to maintain a constant speed in spite of variations in the load, incorporates negative feed-back.

From what has been said about comparing successive attempts at solution, it is clear that some method of storing results will be necessary at various stages of operation of the machine, and in fact the design of suitable types of 'memory,' as it is frequently called, forms one of the most interesting features. In particular, two kinds of memory are generally incorporated; a very high speed 'memory' system of limited capacity from which we can tap off data practically instantaneously, and a secondary storage system of very much greater capacity from which, however, the data are not quite so immediately available. Thus the high speed 'memory' for one computer is provided by cylinders revolving about 100 times per second; the data is impressed instantaneously by variation of the magnetism on the cylinder surface. So long as the magnetism is not subsequently altered the information can be picked up on a magnetically sensitive device at any time within 1/100th of a second.

It will probably be apparent already that there are certain suggestive resemblances between computing machines and human brains and of these more will be said later. In any case another feature that we shall have to incorporate in our machine is immediately suggested by this analogy. Our own brain requires to have lines of communication (the nervous system) connecting it to our eyes, hands, etc., which are in contact with the world around us so that it can receive in a suitable way information about the outside world.

In the same way, the automatic computer will clearly require to have some means by which data required for a given calculation can be presented to it in a form which the machine can absorb. Various methods are in fact employed, such as the operation of vast switchboard panels or the use of standardized punched cards; steel tape on which the information can be impressed by continuous variations in the magnetism has also been brought into service. Similarly the final results can be delivered by the machine to the operator in much the same forms or else printed on recording paper.

The actual operation of translating a mathematical or physical problem into the form suitable for a computer demands a high degree of intelligence and the form in which the problem is presented to the machine may make a tremendous difference to the time involved in obtaining the solution. This art is known as 'programming' and in really large-scale problems it is well worth while spending many days in considering the best 'programme' to be adopted.

POTENTIALITIES OF ELECTRONIC COMPUTERS

Let us now consider some of the special characteristics and potentialities of these machines. We can summarize the obvious advantages as follows:

1. Very high speed of operation—so high indeed that many problems of a theoretical character in pure

and applied science can now be readily tackled, which previously would have taken impossibly long times to solve.

2. Freedom from errors. The machine *can*, of course, occasionally develop a fault and make a mistake at some step in the calculations, but it can be readily made to check its working at various stages by a process rather similar to that already outlined, in which the machine obtained progressively better solutions to a problem.

3. Freedom from laziness. The machine does not get tired on a hot summer's afternoon, and this has also the advantage that unavoidable errors due to laziness do not arise. Finally,

4. Freedom from 'nerves.' This must be qualified to some extent because by some maladjustment of the machine it is possible for it to simulate a condition which we might liken to a nervous breakdown in a human being. We might, for example, 'tease' a machine to go on seeking a worse and worse solution to a problem, and this might finally lead to a catastrophic condition of the machine.

In assessing the possible fields of application for these machines we must at present, at least, inevitably count the cost; a machine embracing many thousands of electronic valves can hardly be an inexpensive item. It is consequently not surprising that the development and employment of these computers are as yet more or less confined to Government laboratories or to very large industrial concerns, although it is somewhat surprising, perhaps, that only one or two universities in this country and in America have so far undertaken the construction of such machines for their own purposes.

Apart from the direct application of glorified adding machines for pure accounting, obvious commercial applications would be in the solution of any problem which, although essentially quite straightforward, involved a large number of interdependent variable quantities, such as perhaps the costing of a range of products or the economical routing of any large transport system. More indirectly, many numerical problems in applied science can be solved quickly by these computers; an early problem solved by an analogue computer in this country was the rapid calculation of train-running times on particular routes given certain locomotive data, the weight of the train, and the gradients of the line. It was then possible to see readily whether locomotive traction power was being used efficiently.

Finally, of course, we may expect industry to benefit in the long run from the solution of many problems in pure science which have so far been denied solution because of their tremendous complexity. Scientific man-power could then be released from rather tedious tasks, such as the calculation of numerical tables, say, of astronomical data or actuarial functions, for work of greater originality.

CAN A MACHINE THINK?

It is of great interest and importance to consider also the more abstract significance and possible future influence of computers. When we review the capabilities we have discussed we are tempted to feel that the machine can look at us and say in the words of the song: 'Anything you can do, I can do better.' However, most of us would reply forthwith: 'Ah, but *I* can think—a machine can't.'

While we may finally come to this conclusion after careful consideration of what we mean by human thought, it is not quite so obvious that a machine cannot think. For it is just the capability of a well-designed and flexible computer to carry out what is essentially a train of logical argument on a set of premises which gives it its tremendous possibilities. A machine has already been demonstrated that cannot be beaten at 'noughts and crosses,' and a recent article discusses the design and programming of a computer which could 'play' a tolerably good game at least of chess. We do not, of course, suggest that any very useful purpose would be served by the actual construction of such a machine, any more than by the construction of a robot which could 'smoke' tobacco. The point is rather one of fundamental principle since, as the author of the article says, the game of chess is an excellent test case. We do generally consider it to be a game in which 'real thought' is involved. Consequently, if we can present a pattern for a machine which would play reasonably well we must either admit that a machine can 'think'—that is, that thought is essentially a mechanized process—or else modify our conception and definition of thought.

It appears quite possible in principle to make provision in a machine for the selection of the legal moves and then for some assessment of a good move according to a preconceived system of valuation. The choice of the best move would, of course, require that the machine could 'think out' many moves ahead, and an enormously complex machine would, in fact, be required for this. In practice even the largest machines available to-day—if suitably programmed—could only 'play' a very mediocre game, far below professional standards. This corresponds with the fact that automatic computers at their *present* stage of development can only tackle a very small fraction of the range of work with which the human brain can deal.

We have thus to realize that the electronic machine is really only in its infancy despite its already considerable powers. The day might come, of course, when two machines could face each other over a chessboard and the match be decided by the first move! It might be well in such an era to prohibit machines from 'playing' games, since evidently much of the variety and spice of life would disappear if mistakes were never made.

Let us now imagine that a very much more advanced form of chess machine has been developed. Would we not still expect any standardized scheme of play to fail under certain circumstances, particularly against a very skilled human opponent? We could then say: '*I* can learn by experience from my mistakes; a machine *cannot*, once you have laid down its conditions of operation.' This objection is untenable, however, since it would in principle be quite possible to include a mechanism by which an error in strategy leading to defeat, or simply to a worsening of the situation, would be 'noted for future reference'—that is, the system of assessing the value of the moves could receive automatic modification after each serious 'mistake.'

An argument in favour of the human brain is that it is a continually evolving fabric—so long as the individual matures or, to put it more simply, the brain is alive. Is not a machine something which we have designed and constructed, and there it is? We may even be forced to abandon this argument, because if we extend the ideas above, we may ultimately be able to conceive of a machine which could in a limited sense add to—and modify—parts of itself, in so far as it meets with success or otherwise in dealing with the problems presented to it. This claim should not perhaps be pressed too far, since machines would, in fact, have to go a very long way before they could begin to compete with the very remarkable reproductive capacity of living tissue. On the other hand, of course, defective vital parts of a machine can be replaced rather more readily than those of a human being!

SUMMING UP

It is from such considerations as these that one may be led to interpret the idea of Purpose, or a guiding principle in any sphere of activity, as essentially just the operation of this automatic error correction or negative feed-back. The application of these ideas, particularly to the human body and brain, roughly defines the study of Cybernetics (the word, by the way, is derived from the Greek word for a navigator). In so far as the study of the behaviour of automatic machines and their capabilities has led, and is leading, to fresh and valuable insight into the actual mechanics of our brain and nervous system there can be little serious objection except when analogies are taken over too glibly, as is sometimes the case.

However, we are inevitably led to consider how far we are prepared to admit in principle that an automatic computer can replace a human brain and, more practically, how far it is an economic proposition to replace a human being in certain functions by a machine.

I

The first question, like all good discussion topics, is still *sub judice*. It does appear that many activities of our brains must ultimately be recognized as fundamentally mechanical in nature, but yet we feel it would be unsound to assume that machines might be able to replace us in everything.

Thus it has been seriously suggested that a machine would be able to cope with the problems of the complex economic struggle which dominates the world and produce a solution, where man alone has not yet succeeded. This is surely wrong. We should not expect that a machine *constructed* by man could solve international problems when the *direct* employment of his mental processes cannot deal with them; what is really required is the application of more scientific, rational, and direct thought on these problems, with perhaps more appreciation of the individual vagaries of the human element. This vital problem defeats the human brain *not* because of the time it would require to solve but rather, it seems, because past data do not suffice for a solution where a constantly evolving civilization is at stake.

To the credit also of the human being, it does seem that he can—at least to some extent!—cope with entirely unexpected or unallowed-for situations, for which it would surely never be possible to provide a wholly adequate programme.

We must also remember that in matters of decision or assessment, the machine has always to be provided with some numerical or obviously quantitative system of 'judgment' on which to work. In this respect, however, human beings might sometimes learn from the machine. Thus it is just as meaningless to ask a human being whether a Beethoven sonata is greater than a Shakespeare sonnet as it would be to 'ask' the machine before an agreed standard of values had been established by common consent.

The problem of the economics of replacing human beings by machines is certainly one which will evolve with the development of the machine. For instance, it might well be possible to devise some kind of elaborate machine to check over a sheet of typescript for errors, but its complication would be so enormous that it would undoubtedly be cheaper to employ a human being—and certainly much easier to produce! It seems rather likely that in this case much time will elapse before it would be economic to devise a machine replacement.

On the other hand, a weather-forecasting computer might well be a reasonable proposition within the next few years. At present one might compute accurately the weather for the next few hours if one was prepared to spend some weeks or months over the problem so as to include practically *every* relevant factor—such forecasts would be of even less value than those we receive to-day! The high-speed operation of a machine, however, might well solve this difficulty for us and one could envisage an entirely automatic organization, equipped with automatic recorders for all the necessary data feeding in to the computer, which would then deliver a continuous forecast pattern.

Tax-gathering suggests another possible, though perhaps somewhat perverted, field of application for the machine because of the complex interplay between a man's desire for a commodity and his degree of docility in paying tax on it. For instance, one can readily appreciate that there is an optimum rate of tax which may be imposed on a specific article for the

greatest tax-yield to result, although alteration of tax on
one item (for example, petrol) may obviously alter the
optimum for another (for example, industrial vehicles).
The machine, with its faculty of dealing with a problem
dependent on a large number of variables would appear
to be most suitable for this task.

We must note, however, that this is a typical problem
in economics, and in such cases the human element
often appears to be human just in that it is unexpected,
or unpredictable. In mathematical terms we would say
that there was a considerable random-element present!
Thus even to-day it is extremely difficult to predict
what tax limit we are prepared to suffer in order to
smoke tobacco although the habit has been known for
hundreds of years. It seems that in any problem
involving human beings or our own social structure
we have to be unusually cautious, because the situation
is continuously evolving and it is very difficult to say
how valid the employment of past economic data is
in attempting to predict future behaviour—however
well-behaved the predictor itself may be!

To sum up, it seems certain that the computer-
machine will progress very much further and we must
be prepared to realize that it will be able to take over
many functions of the human brain which to-day we
should certainly call 'thinking.' It is impossible to
predict how far along the road to 'braininess' a machine
may ultimately travel; it is clear, however, that the
unit element will have to be much reduced in size as
time goes on or the machines will grow to unmanage-
able proportions; steps have already been taken in this
direction. One may perhaps ask what a world 'popu-
lated' with super-machines will be like, what we shall
do then, and whether it may not become rather a dull

world. However, one might apply a remark of Mr. Churchill's and suggest that the difficulties should be left to argue for themselves.

None the less, it is clear that these machines have a very significant role to play at the present time, and industry must seriously consider how best to take advantage of their present capabilities both in research and in administration.

CAN THE WORLD'S POPULATION
BE FED?[1]

SOMEWHERE in the Pacific there is a tiny island occupied only by goats—all descended from a few left there by the crew of some ship. They have multiplied, feeding on the scarce grass, and now a few hundred goats live there miserably, as many dying from malnutrition as are born. Such a state of affairs would not have arisen as part of a natural development. In any natural equilibrium some predatory animal would also have had a place, with the effect that there would be fewer goats there—but they would be living a happier life! Only man has the ability to upset natural equilibrium. But does he use his ability to re-establish equilibrium in his own affairs? We have only to look at India or Egypt to see that he does not —these countries only too obviously resemble Goat Island. Now that the major check, disease, has been largely eliminated, man has done nothing to stop the growth of population.

The control of population is difficult, of course, because procreation is so intimately connected with other aspects of social life. But even without this, matters would be difficult enough. There exists a metaphysical belief, fostered by many religions, that to reach the maximum number of 'souls' is a desirable aim, while the quality of the souls, or of the bodies attached to them, seems to be only a secondary consideration. Power politics by Governments has

[1] Written in June 1949, but not published.

also encouraged high birth-rates, the emphasis this time being perhaps mainly on the bodies.

Now in earlier times the encouragement of unchecked increase of population might perhaps have been the right thing. The trouble here, as in so many other things, is that notions which might at one time have been correct, become hardened into taboos and are mistaken for everlasting truths. The whole question of birth-control is still dealt with in great parts of the world on an emotional level, and the writer remembers well the effect when some ten years ago in a highly educated circle he defended the thesis that doctors who fought diseases in over-populated regions were the worst enemies of the people whom they tried to help if they did not at the same time introduce their patients to methods of birth-control, and if they thought this was impossible, they should keep away altogether.

Malthus foresaw much of the trouble about 150 years ago, although not all his predictions came true because of the scientific improvement in agriculture introduced since. Also, just as important, enormous new tracts of arable land have been put under the plough, particularly in the Americas, with the help of mechanization.

But what is the position now? The earth harbours at present a population of about 2,200 million and the number is increasing by about 20 million each year. To feed everyone properly, even at the present time, about twice as much food will have to be produced. Are there any prospects of achieving this and of keeping up with the ever-increasing numbers?

Let us first consider how far we can go in principle, with our existing resources of chemicals and solar energy. Here the answer is quite certain. We are still a very long way off the ultimate limit to our population. A growing population will, it is true, have to make do with less proteins—particularly animal proteins—but it is probable that a sufficient diet could be provided for a population at least five times as great as the present world population. By the time this figure is reached it will probably be possible to synthesize food so that still more people could be fed—though it is highly questionable whether such a crowded world would be desirable from any point of view.

However, while a supply of certain chemical elements, and of solar energy, are essential for the growing of food, this is not the whole story. Up to the present time at least, and certainly for some time to come, soil is also needed for the growing of plants, and the availability of suitable soil will be all-important for at least the next 100 years or so. This absolutely vital question has lately been discussed in a number of books. Perhaps the best known is *The Road to Survival* by Vogt, head of the Conservation Section of the Pan-American Union. In this book an analysis is made of the 'resource capital' of our food production and of how it is used. It is shown in examples, mainly drawn from the Americas, how destructive are prevalent agricultural practices, and in particular how the top soil is being destroyed at an appalling rate by faulty agricultural methods, by over-grazing, and by deforestation which upsets the water balance. Top soil accumulated by nature over millions of years can be blown away, or run into the ocean, in a matter of years.

While this has been known to experts for some time and the main merit of the book lies in presenting the facts—perhaps somewhat over-dramatized—in a digestible and interesting form for the general public, there are also many points raised which are so far new to most people. In particular, the dangerous position of most of the countries of South America was unknown to the writer, and Vogt has many hard words to say about those of his countrymen who exploit the resources of that continent in such an irresponsible way.

The only remedy for the major world problem with which we are presented lies in the application of drastic measures both in population and in agricultural policy. Let us consider the latter question in a little more detail. There is bound to be stiff resistance to any proposal put forward, and we must know the facts in order to combat this. Opponents of the measures necessary will no doubt say that Vogt's picture is too pessimistic. They will point out that science has been able to increase the output per acre steadily and will go on doing so.

There are, of course, many ways in which food production can be increased relatively quickly. The proper study of plant genetics will give us new improved strains with increased resistance to disease and able to thrive over a wider range of temperatures. Pests and weeds can now be combated by new synthetic chemicals of high activity. (Here, however, we must be on our guard. These chemicals also destroy useful insects and plants, and thus upset the biological equilibrium, with possible far-reaching effects. We already hear warning notes from the United States, and we must bear in mind that some of these effects may appear only after very prolonged periods.)

The statement that the virgin land which has so far been drawn on is now more or less exhausted will be countered with the statement that artificial irrigation can bring large new tracts of land into the picture. Up to a point this is certainly true, but irrigation is an expensive matter, and the necessary installations will take a long time to build.

Of course, the present output of food can be considerably increased, and, indeed, it must be if serious trouble is to be avoided in the quite near future. However, we must make quite sure that short-term improvements do not continue to be made at the expense of future fertility. It is difficult enough to see how the gap can be closed in the near future, but the general trends in these matters are still more alarming, especially if we consider the accelerated rise in population which is to be expected as a result of recent developments in medical science.

However, everyone must judge for himself. A study of the books published on this subject is essential for anyone who wants to see for himself what the world is heading for. These books introduce the public to a new kind of thinking which will become more and more necessary now that the world is filling up and inter-relations between its parts become closer. The time has passed when a man could be called an expert who understood his own specialized job, but did not consider the integral problem. One now has to treat the whole patient, not only the particular disease, and in trying to understand this problem one has to think in terms of real values, not fictitious ones.

It is true that nearly everyone now understands that what is needed is a World-State, perhaps attained in steps via a United Europe. What most people still do not realize is that the larger units cannot simply remain loose affiliations. There must be unified control on matters such as population and agricultural policy, since these matters affect the well-being of all. One does not need traffic lights if only ten horse-driven carriages pass over a crossing every hour, but when ten motor cars pass every minute things are quite different. No one regards traffic lights as an infringement of his personal freedom. But people who think the price of a world population and agricultural policy is too high, will have to realize that the only alternative is to turn the clock back to the days of the horse-drawn carriage.

If a World-State does not come about, and the world divides into two or more pieces, the question of who will survive in the long run may not depend so much on questions of ideology, but on which group treats his resources in the most scientific way. We should remember that the Russians have first-class soil scientists and that they are accustomed to the application of science to practical problems.

If the democratic way of life is to survive, democracies must also be able to take vigorous action. Governments generally do this only when forced by public opinion. The problem under discussion is of vital importance to all of us, and it is essential that a well-informed public opinion be built up in this matter.

SOME REFLECTIONS ON ACCURACY[1]

I AM on holiday and it is raining, so I now read my paper properly instead of skimming through it. I learn that there was a fire in a French factory yesterday and—'the damage is estimated at £116,000.' How do they know so soon? Remembering that the rate of exchange is Frs.864 to the pound, I take my slide rule (about which later) and calculate that the original news must have said that the damage was estimated at 100 million francs. The translator simply divided 100 million francs by 864 and we can only be grateful that he stopped dividing before reaching the shillings and pence.

I read on and see in the headlines the news of an oil company's bumper profits. The directors are congratulated on the fact that 'the profits have risen to £18,564,857 and are nearly double those of the previous year.' I feel sure, however, that we should think the directors worthy of the same congratulations if the profits had been only £18,564,856 or if we saw any other figures in the last five or six places! The report adds that this result has been achieved 'although output only rose from 19,189,551 to around 20,000,000 tons.' I am relieved to find that it does not continue by saying that this means an increase of only around 810,449 tons.

Actually, subtractions of two figures of different accuracy are relatively rare; adding such figures is, however, quite common practice and, indeed, seems to play an essential part in drawing up most cost estimates.

[1] *Financial Times*, August 20, 1948.

I remember one such estimate for a building at £86,356 11s. 6d.—incidentally it was later exceeded by about £20,000. It is obvious—particularly when one has an idea how these estimates are arrived at—that to quote such a figure is either nonsense or hypocrisy, but perhaps I am not sufficiently acquainted with the law of libel and had better not pursue this point.

One can observe the workings of similar minds in many other fields. During these rainy days I have been dipping into an almanack and I have come across a table giving the population of the different provinces of China. Most of the figures are in round millions and probably even this claims too high an accuracy. Among the figures are those for a few smaller provinces where counting was obviously simpler—for instance, one with a population of 312,000. Finally, all these figures are added together and the estimated population of China in 1946 is given as 456,582,000—what nonsense!

Curiously enough, most people feel that a number which looks exact is better than a rounded number. This is quite wrong. When one writes down a number relating to some observation or fact, the accuracy claimed is implied in the way the number is written. The last digit which is not zero is supposed to be known correctly. For instance, in our first example, to say that the damage is estimated at £116,000 should really mean that it is fairly certain to be between £115,000 and £117,000. Similarly the statement on the population of China should mean that it is known to be 456,582,000 and not to be 456,583,000.

The original estimate of the damage as 100 million francs, of course, meant that the damage was anything between, say, 50 and 150 million francs, and a reasonable translation would have been 'about £100,000.' The population of China with its teeming millions cannot be ascertained more closely than to the nearest million, or even to the nearest 10 million or more, particularly with the present state of affairs in China. To say more than that it is of the order of 450 million, or perhaps between 450 and 460 million is definitely wrong.

The example of the oil company is slightly different. Of course, the company's accountants must know the profit exactly, and I do not suggest that accounts should be kept inaccurately. When, however, the financial position of such a company is discussed in an article for the general public it is superfluous and annoying to have to read these figures. It tells us enough, and makes better reading, if it is stated that the profit has risen to £$18\frac{1}{2}$ million, and that the output has risen from about 19 million to around 20 million tons.

Actually there are very few quantities in everyday life which we determine with an accuracy of 1 in 1,000 —in most cases the accuracy is only about 1 per cent. When I buy a piece of material the salesman certainly does not measure its length with a closer accuracy than $\frac{1}{2}$ per cent. The calorific value of my coal, which after all is its most important quality for me, varies by many per cent (even though its weight may be within 1 per cent of the supposed value). But I have to pay my bill of, say, £5 with an accuracy of 1 in 1,000. The reason is that while the physical quantities cannot easily be measured with a high accuracy, the bill can easily be made out in terms of the smallest units, say 1d., and the number of these units can be counted with any desired accuracy. Once the bill has been made out, the 1d. has to be carried through to the bitter end, but more consideration should surely be given when writing out the bill to the fact that the actual value of the goods sold is generally not so precisely fixed.

It is a pity that the ideas of accuracy obviously accepted in the business world prevent business men using a calculating device which has become the inseparable companion of all scientists and engineers— the slide rule. This is a device by which multiplication and division can be performed with very great speed. The technique of using the slide rule is very easily learned, and the smaller types can be carried comfortably in the pocket. It is true that the accuracy is limited, with the larger types to about 1 in 1,000 and with smaller ones to 2 or 3 in 1,000. However, since this is about the accuracy with which everyday things are usually determined it should be sufficient for most purposes.

The main purpose of the slide rule, however, is not in detailed or accurate calculations, but to find out quickly the rough magnitude of a quantity, generally in order to see whether it is likely to be of importance in a particular problem. This would be very useful to business men, who often need to make such rapid estimates, and now generally have to use rather cumbersome methods.

It is still raining and I am turning the pages of the almanack. I find that China's imports in 1946 were of the value of 1,501,160,000 Chinese dollars; the population of India in 1941 was 388,977,955 (if this last statement is to mean anything at all, the exact time of the counting should have been stated, as India's population *increases* by about ten to fifteen persons per minute!); the greatest depth of the Atlantic Ocean is 27,962 feet; the estimated revenue of Poland for 1946 was 35,485,128,077 zloty. I begin to wonder why the